Basic concepts
in quantum mechanics

Translation editor's preface

Quantum Mechanical concepts underlie many of the most startling and exciting discoveries in the world of science and technology. The basic ideas of quantum mechanics are readily accessible to the student who can understand physical optics. This requires that he abandon many concepts that apply to macroscopic objects when he considers phenomena on the atomic and subatomic scale. Professor Kompaneyets has given here a splendidly clear presentation of these fundamental notions with a minimum of mathematics. He has even been able to outline some of the more arcane areas of the subject such as quantum field theory and to give some feeling for the concepts involved.

Students in elementary physics and chemistry should be able to read and absorb the material with little difficulty. This is not limited only to the person majoring in physics or chemistry, for there is no calculus and the subject is developed with the use of analogies to familiar ideas in light and sound.

Changes from the Russian original have been kept minimal; where changes have been made, they have been in the interests of clarity and precision. These have been incorporated into the text and no attempt has been made to distinguish between the original and the revisions since it would have been detrimental to the basic pedagogical purpose of the book.

LEON F. LANDOVITZ

January, 1966

Basic concepts
in quantum mechanics

ALEXANDER S. KOMPANEYETS
Professor of Physics
Institute of Chemical Physics of the Academy of Sciences
U.S.S.R.

Translation editor: LEON F. LANDOVITZ
Yeshiva University
New York, N. Y.

Translated by Scripta Technica, Inc.
Translation read and approved by the author

New York
REINHOLD PUBLISHING CORPORATION
Chapman & Hall Ltd., London

Preface

Spectacular advances have been made by the science of physics in our own time. These include not only the enormous technological progress, somewhat anticipated by man's desires (television, to mention one such instance) but, above all, the emergence of towering generalized concepts brought forth by human thought. Such ideas are a part of existing reality, inasmuch as they reflect the true laws of nature. These ideas alone have enabled modern science to explore and penetrate the innermost nature of matter.

It has been suggested that modern theories of physics are difficult to expound in easy-to-understand terms, because their basic concepts, unlike those of the old classical theories, cannot be readily visualized. In classical physics too, however, there are quite a few concepts that seem to be easily visualized only because we have somehow become accustomed to them (heat capacity or magnetic field intensity are good examples). There is little doubt that the concepts of quantum physics could eventually be rendered no less accessible to visualization. The challenge, however, must be met here by the educator rather than by the scientist. To be sure, some of the more intricate mathematical derivations will have to be taken for granted, but there is no harm in that as long as their meaning, in terms of physics, has been made clear.

The prospect is a tempting one, when we consider that to

this day the students in some schools are still being presented with the same, hopelessly outdated Bohr's model of the atom with its orbitals, for which there really is no physical justification.

This supplementary book is intended for introductory physics courses. It is assumed that the student has already studied the elementary concepts of wave motion, since the author feels that such concepts are basic to the understanding of quantum theory. The author's aim is to show that the basic concepts of quantum mechanics can be defined without recourse to higher mathematics. The main difficulty for the reader will lie here in assimilating some of the entirely novel concepts associated with quantum mechanics. Should he prove equal to the challenge, an unparalleled achievement of the human mind will be his to contemplate—a unique feat that has altered all of our ideas on the nature of motion.

The exposition of material in this book follows a systematic conceptual, rather than historic, sequence. Ideas presented in their logical continuity will be grasped more fully. As we go along, however, an occasional excursion into history proves to be useful. The inevitable evolution of ideas can be better understood when viewed in retrospect.

ALEXANDER S. KOMPANEYETS

Contents

1 Geometric and wave optics

When speaking of motion, we generally visualize a body or a "point" moving in space along some trajectory. However, in nature we encounter just as often another form of motion—wave motion, which can either be perceived by the eye (light), or the ear (sound).

In the final analysis, seeing is connected with the process of wave propagation. Everyone probably knows that light consists of electromagnetic oscillations, i.e., periodic variations in the electromagnetic field in space and in time. However, people have not always associated the propagation of light with wave motion. Isaac Newton, the founder of mechanics, as well as of physical optics, supposed that light is carried by a stream of particles or *corpuscles*. The two words have the same meaning, but "corpuscle" emphasizes the special nature of light particles. In fact, a wide range of optical phenomena can be explained with the aid of the particle concept. This branch of optics is called geometric optics; the trajectories of the corpuscles correspond to rays of light. For example, a ray of light in a homogeneous medium travels in a straight line, and a particle also travels in a straight line when there are no forces acting on it.

The action of mirrors is based on the law of light reflection: i.e., the angle of incidence α is equal to the angle of reflection β (Fig. 1). The same law holds for the elastic reflection of par-

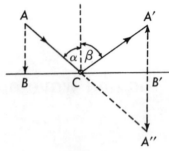

Figure 1

ticles from a barrier; this law can be illustrated by a ball bouncing off a wall, or by a billiard ball off the cushion.

If one considers how the law of reflection of particles follows from the general principles of mechanics, one must first assume that the reflection is elastic, which means that the kinetic energy of the body is conserved on impact. The kinetic energy, on the other hand, is equal to half the product of the mass by the square of the velocity. However, since mass is also conserved, the magnitude of the velocity will remain unchanged. The velocity of the particle at impact on a barrier is represented in Figure 1 by AC, the square of which (the square of the velocity) equals the sum of the squares of its components: $(AC)^2 = (AB)^2 + (BC)^2$.

It will now be shown that the tangential component of the velocity (in this case BC) remains unaltered on impact. For this it is necessary to assume that the reflecting surface is perfectly smooth, i.e., that there are no frictional forces that would change the motion of the particle in the direction parallel to the surface. If there are no such forces, then, by Newton's second law of motion, the component of momentum* in this direction will also be conserved. Consequently, the component of velocity in the direction parallel to the reflecting surface will be conserved ($CB' = CB$).

---

* Momentum = mass $\times$ velocity.

In the right triangles ABC and $A'CB'$ we have $AC = CA'$ by the law of conservation of energy (the square of the velocity remains the same), and $BC = CB'$ by the law of conservation of momentum.

Hence the remaining sides AB and $A'B'$ are also equal in length but not in direction (like AB and $B'A''$), since a co-incidence in direction would mean that the body was not reflected from the surface but has penetrated the reflecting medium (point A''). $B'A'$ must therefore point upward. Since the triangles are congruent, it follows that the angles also are equal and hence $\alpha = \beta$. Later the same law will be deduced from the wave theory of light.

The action of lenses, which depends upon the refraction of light, can also be described in terms of ray optics. The fundamental law of refraction (Snell's law) may be deduced from the corpuscular hypothesis as follows.

Let us suppose that in a denser medium the particle has a *higher* velocity. In effect, this is the way an optically dense medium is defined in the *corpuscular* theory of light. The component of velocity along the boundary between two media must be conserved ($BC = CB'$) for the same reason as in the case of reflection (no retarding force parallel to the boundary). In Figure 2, CA' represents the velocity after refraction. For

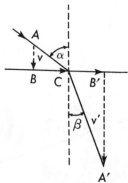

Figure 2

this to be greater than the velocity before refraction, $B'A'$ must be longer than BA, so that the angle β is less than the angle α, which is required by Snell's law for the denser medium. Since $BC = CB'$, it follows that $v \sin \alpha = v' \sin \beta$, so that the ratio of the sines of the angles of incidence and refraction is equal to the ratio of the velocities in the two media. This will be a constant for the two given media, from which follows Snell's law.

In order for the angle of refraction to be less than the angle of incidence, the corpuscular theory requires the velocity of light in a relatively dense medium, such as water or glass, to be greater than in a vacuum. However, an experiment performed by Foucault in the middle of the last century showed that the velocity of light in water is less than in air. It would have been impossible to perform a direct experiment of this kind not only in Newton's day, but for a century and a half after him. Hence the corpuscular theory of light attracted many adherents. Not only was it consistent with experience, but all the applied optics of that era belonged to the field of ray, or geometric optics, which was concerned with optical instruments, such as telescopes and microscopes.

Even in Newton's time, however, certain known light phenomena could not be explained by the corpuscular theory. Newton discovered and described one of these phenomena himself. If a convex lens is placed on a plane glass surface (Fig. 3a), a system of bright and dark rings can be observed in reflected light around the point of contact (Fig. 3b). It is impossible to explain how these rings are formed purely in terms of the laws of refraction and reflection of light.

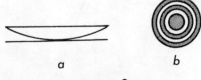

a   b

Figure 3

Newton supposed that light is propagated in what he called "fits," but it is difficult to say what he meant by this. Evidently, even for Newton's successors, who accepted his corpuscular theory of light, the meaning of these "fits" was obscure.

Huygens, a contemporary of Newton, introduced a wave theory of light, by which he explained not only the refraction and reflection of light, but also Newton's rings and related phenomena.

It might appear impossible to formulate the laws of ray optics, such as Snell's law, in terms of waves. The two seem to have little in common: a moving wave front is a surface and a ray is a line. In fact, however, a correspondence between them can be easily established. The ray at a given point in space is perpendicular to the wave front at that point. When a stone is dropped into water, circular ripples travel out from the point where the stone entered. Each circle is a wave front, and the radius drawn from the center to the circle is a ray (Latin, *radius*). Of course, the circles or waves are a visible reality, while the radius is an imaginary line.

When a ship is moving through water, its prow sets up a system of circular ripples at every instant, so that waves created at different instants may arrive simultaneously at a given point. The only exceptions are the points lying on a common tangent to all the circles and passing through the prow of the ship (Fig. 4). (The ship is assumed to be moving faster than the waves it sets up, or else the waves would all lie one inside the other.) Every point of this tangent is reached by only one

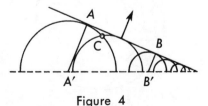

Figure 4

wave front—the most forward one (the others are unable to reach it). For example, the wave arriving at point A was created when the prow of the ship was at point A', while the wave arriving at B was set up when the prow was at B', and so on. The waves arriving at point C between them were set up at different times, and the crests of some waves are superimposed upon the troughs of others, so that the resultant wave at C may be weakened in comparison with the wave front. On the other hand, there is a wave crest everywhere along the line AB, but now it is not circular but rectilinear. The crest moves forward through the water in the direction shown by the arrow, parallel to the radii AA' and BB'.

Thus when circular waves are superimposed, they may form a rectilinear wave front. The waves propagated from a point source in space are spherical, but if sources are distributed on a plane and emit waves together (a more detailed definition will be given), then the front will also be plane and parallel to the plane of the sources.

Huygens did not know the exact law of emission and propagation of waves, which was only discovered about 20 years later. For purely intuitive reasons he assumed that each point on a wave front is itself a source of waves. Figure 5 illustrates this idea for a circular front. Here A is the wave front at a particular time (the waves emitted in accordance with Huygens' hypothesis are indicated by the broken lines), and B

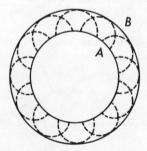

Figure 5

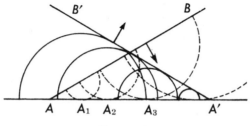

Figure 6

is the envelope forming the wave front of these new waves at a subsequent time. Waves in three dimensions are propagated in a similar way.

The diagram that has been considered provides a qualitative description of the propagation of waves. Huygens' hypothesis gives the simplest explanation of optical phenomena without recourse to complicated calculations. Rigorous equations usually give only small corrections to the results obtained by the simple application of Huygens' principle.

Reflection will be considered first (Fig. 6). According to Huygens' principle, each point on the incident wave front AB may be considered as a source of new waves. As the point A is displaced to the right, taking successively the positions A_1, A_2, A_3, etc., it emits new waves all the time. The common tangent of these waves is the reflected wave front $A'B'$. It can readily be verified that the incident and the reflected wave fronts are inclined at equal angles to the reflecting surface AA'. It could not be otherwise, since both waves are propagated in the same medium and therefore have the same velocity; but if the lines AB and $A'B'$ form equal angles with the reflecting surface, the perpendiculars to these lines, indicated by the arrows, will also form equal angles to it. Thus the law of reflection has been deduced from the wave representation, which in the given case is equivalent to the ray representation.

The law of refraction may be deduced just as simply (Fig. 7). Waves from point A enter the second medium lying below

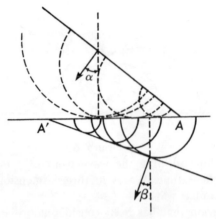

Figure 7

the dividing boundary AA'. If one supposes that the second medium is optically denser, in accordance with Snell's law, angle β must be less than angle α. The refracted wave front must therefore make a smaller angle with the boundary AA' than with the incident wave front. It is immediately clear from the diagram that for this to be true, the velocity of the waves in the second medium must be *less* than in the first. The refracted ray, indicated by the lower arrow, will then lie closer to the perpendicular to the dividing boundary. Consequently the wave representation of light requires a lower velocity in an optically denser medium. As previously seen, the corpuscular representation leads to the opposite conclusion.

Thus the wave theory is also capable of explaining the refraction of light. The law of refraction has the same form as in the corpuscular theory, but the ratio of the sines is not now equal to the reciprocal of the ratio of the wave velocities, but to the ratio of the velocities itself. Hence, according to the wave theory, the velocity of light in water is less than in air. This is in agreement with Foucault's experiment.

It is then seen that the ray (or corpuscular) representation certainly reflects some part of the truth although it is clearly incompatible with the wave representation. It must not be forgotten, however, that design calculation for many optical devices—telescopes, cameras, etc., are based on the ray theory. This agreement is explained primarily by the one-to-one correspondence between the plane wave front and the ray perpendicular to it. It follows that whenever a plane wave front can be drawn through a point of a light wave, a ray of light may also be drawn through that point. One does not have to consider whether there is some kind of particle or material point moving along the ray. Although in the case of light this certainly does not happen, the laws of ray optics are widely applicable. Great success has been achieved in recent decades in electron optics, where images are formed not by rays of light but by beams of moving electrons (e.g., in a television set), and the ordinary laws of geometric optics have been verified in quite another physical region. Later it will be shown that they are even more valid for electrons than for light. This means that far greater magnifications can be obtained in electron microscopes than those possible with ordinary light microscopes, so that even the fine structure of cells of organisms can be revealed.

We have thus found that the laws of optics and mechanics are in many ways equivalent. The same phenomenon may be explained equally well from the two points of view—the corpuscular and the wave—without considering which is the true explanation. Nothing is changed if we replace the constructions of electron optics with a wave representation in terms of Huygens' principle, or if we speak of the paths of light corpuscles in a camera. (When we discuss the path of the rays in a camera we are not at all interested in the velocity of light in the lens.) This one-to-one correspondence was found as early as 1825 by W. R. Hamilton, but the true significance of the analogy he formulated did not become clear until a century later.

As previously stated, not by any means can all light phenomena be described on the basis of geometric optics. One

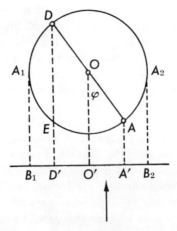

Figure 8

case has already been given—Newton's rings, which can only be explained by the wave theory. Before explaining them, however, we must first consider the fundamental properties of waves and oscillations.

Let us begin with the basic definitions regarding the oscillatory motion of a point. In the discussion we shall encounter the *simple harmonic oscillation* (so named because these oscillations correspond to pure tones in acoustics) far more than any other kind.

Consider a point A moving in a circle (Fig. 8) of unit radius and making ν revolutions per second. Since the circumference of a circle of unit radius is equal to 2π, the point travels a distance of $2\pi\nu$ every second. Let us look at the point in the plane of the figure. The displacement of its projection (point A') will lie between the extreme points B_1 and B_2, which define the *amplitude* or range of the oscillations of the point. In the extreme positions (A_1 and A_2), the velocity of A' moving along the line is zero—the point changes direction and goes back the way it came. At these instants, A is moving along the line of sight (we are looking at it in the direction indicated by the arrow), so that the component of its velocity along the line B_1B_2 is zero. At the point O', the component of the velocity along the line of sight is a maximum.

The oscillations of the point A' are said to be harmonic. The angle $O'OA = \phi$ is called the *phase* of the oscillation, and v is its *frequency*.

Thus v is the number of oscillations per second, and $\omega = 2\pi v$ is the change in phase per second. The phase angle may, of course, be reckoned from any position, not necessarily from OO'. The point D differs from A by a phase of π (in radian measure, or $180°$ in angular measure). Consequently, we also say that the point D' differs in phase from A' by π, or that they are in opposite phase. Points A' and D' are the same distance from O', but on opposite sides of it; their velocities are opposite in sign but equal in magnitude. The projection of the point E, however, moves in the same direction as the projection of A, even though the projections themselves are equal and opposite. Therefore the phases of the projections of E and A are not opposite; in fact, the phase difference is $2\pi - 2\phi$.

The properties of simple harmonic oscillations are as follows:

1. They are characterized by their amplitude and frequency.
2. The position of the oscillating point is prescribed by its phase.
3. To each phase there corresponds an opposite phase.
4. The phase may be reckoned from any position of the point.

We shall require these definitions in quantum mechanics, although there they will not refer to an oscillating point.

Considering wave motion within the same kinematic framework, we shall discuss the rotation, not of a single point, but of a transparent cylinder on the lateral surface of which there is a helical line $A_1A_2A_3A_4A_5 \ldots$ (Fig. 9). If the cylinder is turned through some angle, the point A_1 will move to B_1, A_2

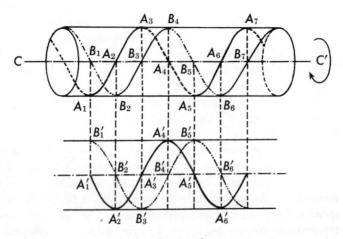

Figure 9

to B_2, etc. We shall use primes to indicate the projections of the points on a plane. The initial position of the helical line will then have the form of the wave $A'_1 \ldots A'_6$, and the position after rotation will be $B'_1 \ldots B'_6$. Now the wave $B'_1 \ldots B'_6$ appears to be displaced to the right with respect to the initial position.

The projection of each point of the helical line onto the plane of the sketch performs simple harmonic oscillations like those just considered. In an infinitely long wave, there are an infinite number of points that are in phase. The distance between any two such neighboring points is called the *wavelength,* which is denoted by the letter λ.

The wavelength is the distance through which the wave advances during one turn of the helix. The helix makes v revolutions per second, so that the wave advances a distance $v\lambda$, and the distance per unit time is the *velocity* c. Thus the velocity of the wave is $c = v\lambda$. For a given velocity, the frequency and wavelength are connected by the inverse relationship $\lambda = c/v$ (it is well known from radio that "short" waves are the same as "high-frequency" waves; wavelengths and frequencies are often shown together on the dial of a radio set). We shall use this connection between wavelength and frequency a great deal.

In comparing the definitions of harmonic oscillations and progressive harmonic waves, we see that in the latter case there is an additional fundamental characteristic—the wavelength or the velocity of propagation. The wave in Figure 9 represents the displacement of a point from the median line. Instead of displacement, we could obtain curves for other quantities, e.g., the velocity of the point. The broken curve in Figure 9 represents the velocity distribution of the points for the same time as the solid curve gives the displacements. (If the broken line is also taken to represent displacements, then it will correspond to a wave displaced by a quarter period from the solid line.) Since the broken curve is displaced by a quarter of a wavelength, it follows that when the displacement is maximum, the velocity of the oscillating point is zero, and vice versa. It is a characteristic of simple harmonic oscillations that the curves of displacement and velocity are identical in form but displaced in phase by $\pi/2$. No other type of oscillation has this property.

A traveling simple harmonic wave may represent not only a kinematic quantity such as position or velocity, but any quantity at all that varies according to this law. For example, in a sound wave corresponding to a pure musical tone produced in a pipe, the compression of the air will be represented by a progressive simple harmonic wave. When overtones of double, triple, etc., frequency are superimposed on the pure tone, a progressive but nonharmonic wave is obtained that will have the same frequency as the harmonic wave. To make Figure 9 refer to a sound wave, we must assume that the crests of the waves refer to the compression of the air and the troughs to rarefactions.

Light sensations in the eye are produced by electromagnetic waves with wavelengths between 0.0004 and 0.0007 mm. Here the oscillating quantities are the intensities of the electric and magnetic fields in space—which has been known since the work of J. C. Maxwell (ca. 1870). Up to that time the principal difficulty of the wave theory of light was the question: what was it that oscillated in a light wave? What physical quantity was varying periodically? Not knowing the answer to this question, Newton, who was acquainted with Huygens' work, could not accept it.

For a long time after Newton many people did not believe in the wave theory for the same reasons as Newton. However, at the beginning of the nineteenth century, Fresnel and Young gave decisive support to the wave theory with their convincing experiments.

These experiments were based on a very important property of waves—their ability to combine. If two waves arrive at some point of space, the resultant displacement (or whatever analogous quantity) is equal to the algebraic sum of the displacements in each wave considered separately. In sound waves the variations in air density are added, and in light waves the variations in the electromagnetic field strength. If the two waves have the same amplitude, and the crest of one wave coincides with the trough of the other at a particular point, then when superimposed they will completely cancel each other out at this point.

Under what conditions can this phenomenon occur? Clearly the waves arriving at the given point must be always in opposite phase to each other. Random canceling at a single instant of time cannot be observed.

How can it be arranged so that the two waves have a constant phase difference? Two sources of light (e.g., two candles or two incandescent lamps) emit their light independently of each other. It is impossible to get them to emit light strictly in phase, i.e., *coherently*. Only very recently has a way been found to cause separate atoms to radiate coherently (in what are known as lasers).

This difficulty may be overcome if a single wave is divided into two waves moving along different paths, and then if the

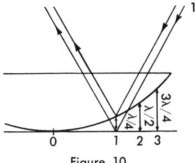

Figure 10

two are combined again. If different numbers of waves can be fitted into these two paths, then after they meet, they will have a time-independent phase difference, i.e., they will be coherent. If the phase difference is equal to an odd integral multiple of π and the amplitudes are equal, then the waves will cancel each other out. In the example of Newton's rings (Fig. 10), the light is partially reflected from each surface dividing different optical media, i.e., from the inner surface of the lens and the outer surface of the glass plate. In the case of ray 1, for example, the wave reflected from the plate always has to travel a length of $\lambda/2$ more than the wave reflected from the spherical surface of the lens ($\lambda/4$ in each direction, down and up). Such waves should cancel each other out; but at the distance 01 from the center we observe a bright ring, not a dark one, while a dark spot is seen at the center.

This does not disprove the wave theory of light but merely shows that in one of the reflections an extra half wave is lost, since the further alternation of rings takes place in the proper order. The changes from bright to dark rings correspond each time to a change in the phase difference between the rays by half a wave, i.e., a change of π. Details on the reasons for losing the half wave on reflection (in this case from the internal surface of the glass) may be found in optics textbooks. The essential fact is that coherent waves are obtained by reflection from two surfaces. Without the concept of coherence and the principle of superposition, it is impossible to understand the origin of Newton's rings.

We must point out a fact that is fundamental to all that follows: the wave nature of light becomes apparent in this experiment because, and only because, the rays are traveling through a region of space comparable in size to the wavelength of light—in this case the thin region between the convex and plane glass surfaces. In this region the phase difference, which varies from ring to ring, is set up.

In the example of Newton's rings, the wave nature of light was revealed only in the alternating rings of brightness and darkness (i.e., a change in the intensity distribution). Here the notion of light rays is not violated, but there are many cases where the very concept of light rays is rendered untenable. Phenomena of this kind, which were studied in detail by Fresnel and Young, dealt a shattering blow to the corpuscular theory of light.

As a typical example, suppose a beam of parallel rays of light strikes a plane opaque screen A with a slit ab (Fig. 11). Working strictly by the principles of ray optics, one would expect to see a band on screen B, equal and parallel to the slit,

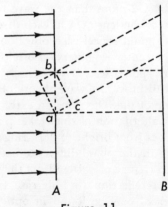

Figure 11

and that the rest of the surface would not be illuminated. In fact the image on screen *B* is much more complicated. The bright band opposite the slit does in fact appear, but in addition there is a system of other bright bands parallel to it. It is easy to perform this experiment: stick a piece of foil on glass and rule a narrow slit on it with a razor; the parallel beam of rays can be produced with a lens having a source of light at its focus, or else by another wider slit illuminated from behind.

How can the bands be explained? Consider the triangle *abc* in which *ab* coincides with the slit and the length of *ac* equals half a wavelength. By Huygens' principle, any point of the wave may be considered as a new source. By construction, waves incident at points *b* and *c* have opposite phases, since the phases at *a* and *b* are the same, and point *c* differs from point *a* by half a wavelength. It follows that on a line joining *b* and *c* there is no other pair of points with opposite phases. Secondary waves emitted by all points on *bc* in accordance with Huygens' principle cannot cancel each other out. As a result the bright band on screen *B* proves to be wider than the slit itself, even when the beam striking *A* is strictly parallel, and the rays that give the bright band beyond the direct projection of *ba* on *B* are no longer parallel but inclined at some angle. It is immediately evident from Figure 11 that this angle is twice the angle *abc* in the triangle, since the waves diverge on either side of the normal to *B*.

The angle *abc* is approximately equal to the ratio of the sides *ac* and *ab*, provided the wavelength is much less than the width of the slit, as is usually the case. The rays are thus inclined to the slit's normal at an angle determined by the ratio of the wavelength and the width of the slit. The breakdown of geometric ray optics again occurs when the wavelength cannot be considered sufficiently small in comparison with the region in which the light is propagated.

Let us now apply Huygens' principle to a triangle in which the side *ac* is equal to a whole wavelength, so that the points *b* and c differ in phase by 2π. Then for each point on the segment bc, another point with opposite phase may be found. Points lying in the first half of the segment will correspond to points of opposite phase in the second half. Consequently, waves proceeding from these points will cancel each other out and no illumination will be obtained on the screen in that direction. This gives the first dark band next to the central bright one. When $ac = 3\lambda/2$, two thirds of the segment bc will correspond to waves that cancel each other out, while one third of the waves will have no waves of opposite phase. Another bright band will be obtained on the screen, although this will be weaker than the central band given by all the points of bc. Further bright bands of decreasing illumination are obtained for $ac = 5\lambda/2$, $7\lambda/2$, etc.

The nonrectilinear propagation of waves is called *diffraction*. The greater the ratio of the wavelength to the size of the slit, the greater the degree of diffraction. For example, sound waves having wavelengths in the 10-100 cm range turn round corners easily and can pass through the crack of a door (or through a keyhole) that has not been completely closed. For effective sound insulation the smallest cracks must be avoided.

If the light source undergoing diffraction is white, the bands will be colored. This is due to waves of different wavelengths diverging at different angles. The long-wave red rays are bent the most and the short-wave violet rays the least.

Diffraction may be used to resolve light into a spectrum. For this purpose one needs a system of slits, called a *diffraction grating* (Fig. 12). Rays coming from each slit will reinforce each other if the path difference between them is one, two, three, etc., wavelengths. A phase difference of one wavelength means, of course, that the waves are completely in phase. If $a_2c_2 - a_1c_1 = a_3c_3 - a_2c_2 = \ldots = \lambda$, a first-order band will be obtained, if this difference equals 2λ, there will be a second-order band, and so on. When the light striking the grating contains many different colors (different wavelengths), each of

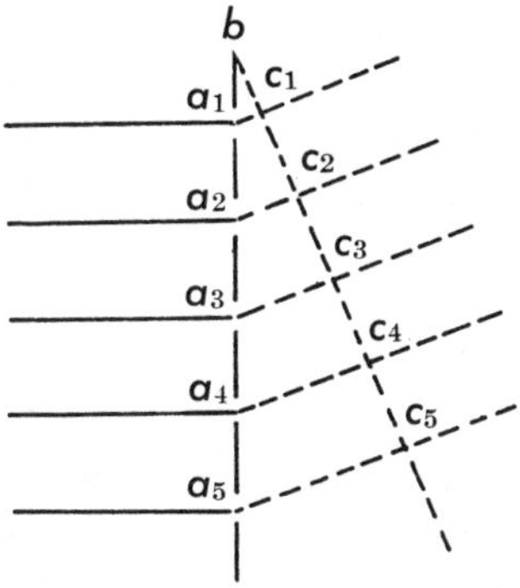

Figure 12

these bands will be resolved into a spectrum. The more slits
or "lines" the diffraction grating has per millimeter, the
greater the distance between the bands, and the better the
resolution of different wavelengths of the spectrum.

The same light wave must pass through all the slits of the
grating, so that its coherence is completely preserved. The
diffraction spectrum is obtained only by the action of the
grating as a whole. This cannot be explained in terms of ray
optics: one ray would pass through one slit and would not, it
would seem, have anything in common with a ray passing
through another slit. However, if we talk about a wave that
possesses a definite phase and compare that phase in different
slits, diffraction becomes completely intelligible. Phase is a
characteristic of a wave and not of a ray—a wave front possesses a definite phase at a given instant of time. Once again, the
breakdown of ray optics arises because the wavelength is comparable with the spacing in the grating. Modern gratings have
several thousand lines per millimeter.

Electromagnetic waves with much smaller wavelengths than
light are called X rays. X-ray diffraction would be very difficult to produce with gratings of the type just discussed. However, crystals can be used as diffraction gratings because their
atoms are arranged in a strict order. This was the explanation

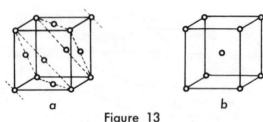

a   b

Figure 13

given for the regular form of crystals long before X-ray diffraction was used to verify the fact that the atoms in crystals do actually form regular lattices in space. In certain substances, e.g., graphite, the lattice consists of sheets placed in a stack. In each sheet the atoms lie at the corners of hexagons, forming a honeycomb pattern. The corners in one sheet lie opposite the centers of the hexagons in the next sheet.

In other lattices the atoms may lie at the corners of cubes and at the centers of their faces (face-centered lattice: Fig. 13a), or at the corners and centers of the cubes (body-centered lattice: Fig. 13b). In both of these arrangements the atoms are more densely packed than in graphite.

Let us now consider a simplified scheme of the X-ray diffraction in a crystal lattice. In any crystal one may select a number of parallel planes in which the atoms are arranged regularly, such as the planes containing the bases of the cubes, or planes passing through the diagonals of the faces. Let us represent this system of planes schematically (Fig. 14a) in the form of a series of horizontal lines. The plane incident wave front is replaced by a single ray AB perpendicular to it. This ray is partially reflected from each plane at points B_1, B_2, B_3, etc., so that reflected rays B_1A_1, B_2A_2, B_3A_3, etc., come from these points. Each of these rays represents its own wave front.

It is clear that the reflected waves will reinforce each other if, and only if, the phase difference between them is equal to $2\pi, 4\pi, 6\pi$, and so on. In all other cases, they cancel each other out, since for every wave front A_n there is some other wave

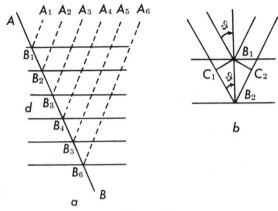

Figure 14

front A_m with opposite phase. Suppose, for example, that the phase difference is 9/10 of 2π and then consider the first and the sixth wave fronts. The phase difference between them is π, which means that wave front A_1 is cancelled by A_6, A_2 by A_7, etc.

Of course, phase differences divisible by 2π are not obtained at every angle of incidence. To obtain the correct phase difference between waves reflected from adjacent planes, let us consider Figure 14b. This is a symmetric representation of two rays reflected from adjacent planes. The wave fronts between them are given by the perpendiculars B_1C_1 and B_1C_2 (the wave front is always perpendicular to the ray). The ray reflected from the lower plane travels along a path that is longer than that of the ray reflected from the upper surface by $C_1B_2 + B_2C_2 = 2B_2C_2$. If the distance between the planes is d, the path difference is clearly equal to $2d \sin \theta$, which in turn must equal $n\lambda$ where n is an integer. Here θ is the angle that the incident and reflected rays make with the plane. The equation $2d \sin \theta = n\lambda$ also defines θ. Reflection from such a system of planes will not take place at any other angle.

By comparing the reflecting power of differently oriented

planes, we may determine exactly from which plane a given reflection takes place. For example, in the plane containing the cube faces, the atoms occur more densely than in other planes through the cube. Hence reflection from the cube faces will be the strongest. X-ray diffraction data for a crystal can be used to determine n and θ in the fundamental equation $2d \sin \theta = n\lambda$. The distributions of atoms in Figures 13a and 13b give different systems of diffraction spots, so that they may be distinguished by their X-ray diffraction photographs. Thus, if the distance between the planes is known, it is easy to find the wavelength of the incident X rays. Conversely, if the wavelength is known, the distribution of the spots defines the structure of the crystal, which is often far more complicated than the cases shown in Figures 13a and 13b.

In order to familiarize the reader with the calculation of atomic constants, we shall show how to determine the distance between the reflecting planes in a cubic lattice of the type shown in Figure 13b. In each cube there are only two atoms, one at the center and one at one of the corners. The atoms at the other corners must be taken as belonging to other cubes. The mass of each atom equals the atomic weight divided by Avogadro's number (6.024×10^{23}), and the mass of the cube is therefore twice as great. The mass per cubic centimeter equals the density of the crystal, and hence the number of cubes per unit volume of the crystal can be easily worked out. This also gives the size of a single cube. Generally, it is of the order of 10^{-8} cm—a characteristic length in atomic physics that will be frequently encountered. This length is comparable with the wavelength of X rays and confirms the general rule: diffraction phenomena arise when the dimensions of the region determining the propagation of the waves are comparable with the wavelength.

2 The uncertainty principle

It was shown in the preceding sections that there are two forms of motion in classical physics: displacement of bodies along trajectories and propagation of waves. The latter cannot always be reduced to the motion of particles in space. Even though waves in water or air can be described by the motion of the particles of the medium, the variation in electromagnetic fields cannot be represented by the displacement of particles. In spite of the difference in these types of motion, the laws governing them are sometimes very similar. This holds when the wavelength is sufficiently small in comparison with the geometric dimensions of the region in which the wave process is propagated. For example, when rays are focused by a lens, the dimensions of the lens are very large in comparison with the wavelength. On the other hand, the region near the focal point may be considered small, and appreciable diffraction phenomena arise there. Again, the images of stars in a telescope are surrounded by diffraction rings, which are impossible to eliminate. These rings are not due to defects of the telescope's optical system that could be eliminated by combining different lenses; diffraction is connected with the wave nature of light.

In the preceding chapter we said that the laws of electron optics, which are, essentially, deduced from the corpuscular theory, can also be established from Huygens' principle if we suppose that the electron motion obeys some wave laws. As long as we are considering large regions, the corpuscular and the wave approaches lead to the same results. What, however, will happen in small regions? In the case of electrons we do not know in advance what dimensions should be considered small: are they the same as in ordinary optics, or are they even smaller?

It turns out that if a beam of electrons is passed through a crystal, the resulting diffraction pattern is the same as that of X rays. In fact, the diffraction of electrons was first observed by Davisson and Germer after Heisenberg and Schrödinger had formulated the laws of quantum mechanics, but we shall give a systematic rather than a historical description. Science does not develop according to a preordained plan; the result, corresponding to an objective state of affairs in nature, is predetermined, although it may be reached in circuitous ways.

We must therefore consider the diffraction of *electrons!* Electrons are beyond doubt not waves but particles—under no circumstances is their charge or mass divided. We can never observe a part of the charge or a part of the mass of an electron, whereas we always regard a wave as a divisible continuous entity. Each electron leaves a single spot on a photographic plate. If we use a beam of very low intensity and pass the electrons one by one through a crystal, the individual spots will be grouped in a single picture that is the same as for the diffraction of X rays. In the same way, a printer's block is made up of individual dots, which when seen as a whole give a clear picture of their subject.

A direct diffraction experiment shows that each electron moves through the lattice like a wave contributing to the diffraction pattern, without ceasing to be an indivisible particle. Although this may seem paradoxical, it is an experimental fact. However, in a number of cases the electron moves purely as a particle, exhibiting no wave properties. For example, in the picture tube of a television set the electrons move along trajectories that, at least in principle, may be predicted as strictly as the orbits of planets. Why then does the electron behave sometimes as a wave and sometimes as a particle?

Let us remember that light too shows this same twofold behavior. When refracted by a lens, it travels in a straight line, but when it strikes a diffraction grating it exhibits its wave nature. All depends upon the ratio between the wavelength and the size of the region in which the motion takes place.

What wavelength, then, corresponds to the motion of an electron? If the same equation as the one for X rays is used, the wavelength may be measured directly from the diffraction pattern. Other atomic particles may also exhibit diffraction, e.g., protons. However, it is more convenient not to transmit protons through a crystal, but to scatter them from the regularly arranged atoms on the crystal surface. This method recalls the diffraction of light rather than of X rays; but here too the diffraction pattern enables us to determine the wavelength. In every case we obtain the following result: the wavelength is inversely proportional to the momentum of the particle, i.e., to the product of its mass and velocity.

The coefficient of proportionality between the wavelength and the momentum of the particle is a universal constant, as important as the elementary charge or the velocity of light. Denoted by the letter h, it is called Planck's constant. In what units is h measured? Since the wavelength equals h divided by the momentum, $\lambda = h/mv$, Planck's constant h must have the dimensions of wavelength multiplied by momentum. Let us find the dimensions of h in the CGS (or MKS) system. Momentum has the dimensions of mass times velocity, i.e., g cm/sec. Hence Planck's constant has the dimensions of g cm^2/sec. We observe that these are the dimensions of energy $\times$ time (energy has the dimensions of g cm^2/sec^2).

Thus in order to find the characteristics of the wave motion of an electron, we must introduce another universal constant into physics. It is universal because it is the same for all particles and for all motions. The wavelength associated with the motion of a proton is expressed in terms of its momentum by the same formula as for an electron (of course, the mass and velocity of the proton are substituted, but Planck's constant remains the same).

Planck's constant describes a law of nature that was not included in Newton's laws. These laws did not contain any universal constants: in saying that force equals mass times acceleration, we do not have in mind any natural units of force, mass, and acceleration (or length, mass, and time in which they may be expressed). Our metric system of measurement is the result of conventions agreed upon by men and does not belong among the laws of physics.

We say, for example, that the meter is $1/(4 \cdot 10^7)$ the length of a meridian of the earth. This is entirely conventional—both the choice of a meridian of the earth as a unit of length and the choice of a forty millionth (and not, let us say, a hundred millionth). But Planck's constant is the same for the whole universe. Consider, for example, Newton's second law, which connects force, mass, and acceleration with the particular motion that we are studying. On the other hand, in the equation $\lambda = h/mv$, Planck's constant h is always the same for any λ, m, and v. Planck's constant occurs in a law connecting physical quantities: wavelength, mass, and velocity. This is truly a law and not a definition of a quantity (like, for example, "momentum equals mass times velocity"). The wavelength is determined from diffraction experiments; the velocity is the distance traveled by the particle in unit time. These quantities are connected by the expression $\lambda = h/mv$, but unlike Newton's laws, they contain the dimensional constant h.

If we take the mass of an electron as the unit of mass and its charge as the unit of charge, then by adding Planck's constant to our list, we may free ourselves completely from the arbitrary units of the metric system. This leads to the atomic system of units. The unit of length in this system is $.52917 \times 10^{-8}$ cm, which is of the same order as the linear dimensions of the atom (cf. end of Chapter One).

Of course, even this system of units still retains an element of convention: why, for example, is the unit of mass taken as the mass of the electron and not the mass of the proton, which is 1836 times greater? We máy also pose the question: why is it exactly this number of times greater? However, it is meaningless to ask why the mass of the electron equals 9.107×10^{-28} g, for the gram is an arbitrary unit, thought up by men. Electrons and protons, on the other hand, exist in nature and do not depend on us. Why the proton is 1836 times heavier than the electron is not known, for still far too little about the structure and interdependence of particles is known.

In the CGS system of units, $h = 6.625 \times 10^{-27}$. The smallness of this quantity in our system of measurement shows how much smaller mechanical quantities are on the atomic scale than on the scale of the quantities encountered in everyday life. Since the value of h is now known, we can answer our fundamental question: why does an electron have wave properties in a crystal but not in a television picture tube? Probably everyone knows that a high voltage—about 20,000 volts—is necessary for a television set. This means that the electrons must reach a high velocity in the picture tube. If we know the voltage applied, can we calculate this velocity?

The voltage is the potential difference in the gap in which the electrons are accelerated. If the charge of the electron is e and the potential difference is ϕ, then it may be shown that as the electron passes through the potential difference ϕ it acquires an energy equal to $e\phi$. Energy is measured in ergs, but since the charge e is a universal constant, the energy of the electron can be measured in units of potential difference, as is usually done in atomic physics. The energy of an electron moving through a potential difference of one volt increases by one electron-volt, abbreviated 1 eV.

Electron-volts can be converted into ergs without difficulty. The charge of an electron equals 4.8026×10^{-10} electrostatic units and a volt equals $1/300$ of an electrostatic unit. Hence one electron-volt equals 1.6×10^{-12} ergs.

An electron in a television picture tube at first has relatively little energy, but it eventually acquires 20,000 eV, which is equivalent to $1.6 \times 10^{-12} \times 2 \times 10^4 = 3.2 \times 10^{-8}$ ergs. However, the energy of a moving electron equals half the product of its mass by the square of its velocity $(mv^2/2)$. Since the mass of the electron is approximately 9×10^{-28} g, we find that the square of the velocity is $3.2 \times 10^{-8}/4.5 \times 10^{-28} = 7.1 \times 10^{19}$ cm²/sec² and the velocity itself is 8.4×10^9 cm/sec. The momentum (mass × velocity) is therefore equal to $9 \times 10^{-28} \times 8.4 \times 10^9 = 7.5 \times 10^{-18}$ g cm/sec. Finally, the wavelength is $\lambda = h/mv = 6.625 \times 10^{-27}/7.5 \times 10^{-18} = 0.89 \times 10^{-9}$ cm.

Now, the diameter of the electron beam in a television set is about 0.1 mm or 10^{-2} cm. This is some 10 million times greater than the corresponding wavelength. Hence it is clear that the wave properties of electrons will not appear in the picture tube, but would certainly give rise to diffraction phenomena if the same electron beam were passed through a crystal. In the television picture tube, the wave properties of electron motion are an unnecessary complication (just as ray optics are quite sufficient for a camera lens*).

The wave properties associated with the motion of electrons in crystals in no way contradict the existence of particle trajectories in other kinds of electronic apparatus.

Let us now consider a very important question: how far may we use the classical concepts of trajectory? Up to now we have only discussed extreme cases: the electron beam in a picture tube, where the classical concept of a trajectory can be used, and diffraction of electrons in a crystal, which cannot be considered, even qualitatively, without the concept of wave motion. In the first case the motion is limited to a region of 0.01 cm, and in the second to the inter planar distance in the crystal (10^{-8} cm). What then is the order of magnitude of a region of motion for which the concept of a trajectory is inapplicable and for which the motion must be considered in terms of a wave?

* But not for a microscope where the objects to be studied are comparable in size with the wavelength of light waves.

Consider the beam of a searchlight. Why do we consider this a geometric ray? Light, of course, is a wave motion in every case, and according to the definition of a searchlight, the waves cannot diverge too far from the direction of the ray. In other words, the concept of a particle trajectory is meaningful when the amplitude of the wave associated with the motion rapidly becomes zero on either side of the trajectory. It is then improbable that we shall find a particle in a place forbidden by the classical (nonwave) laws. In the example illustrated in Figure 11 we considered the effect of a lateral restriction on the propagation of waves. Only an infinitely wide beam of rays can be strictly parallel, but then it has no lateral boundary. Only such a beam corresponds to a perfectly plane wave front, which gives a single, precisely defined direction of wave propagation. (The beam of a projector, or a radar beam, is bounded at the sides, and is therefore only approximately parallel.) The momentum of the particle coincides with this direction, and hence a particle for which the momentum is defined precisely with respect to magnitude and direction has no defined position, i.e., the beam in this case is infinitely wide, with its "trajectory" extending through all space.

If we wish to define the position of the particle in at least one plane, we have to make it pass through a slit in that plane. What happens then? In the example considered in Chapter One (Fig. 11) we saw that if the slit is of breadth d, the wave coming out of it is not strictly parallel, but lies within an angle approximately equal to $\lambda/2d$ (in the same notation as in Fig. 11). Further, $ac = \lambda/2$, $ab = d =$ breadth of the slit. If we assume that the ratio ac/ab is small, the angle of span of the beam that has passed the slit is clearly small too.

In what direction does the velocity of a particle lie after it has passed through the slit? As we have just seen, the only particle possessing a strictly defined velocity direction is one whose motion suffers no lateral restriction. If the wave emerging from the slit is not strictly parallel, but lies within some angle, then the direction of the velocity of the particle also lies within that angle. However, if the velocity, being a vector, is inclined at some small angle, then it has a perpendicular component, approximately equal to the product of the velocity and that angle. Hence after passing through a slit of breadth *d,* the velocity of the particle undergoes a certain deviation in the plane of the slit, although we do not know, of course, at precisely what angle the particle is moving. It will be moving *somewhere* within the angle defined by the diffraction relationships.

We may therefore say that the velocity possesses an uncertainty. The position of the particle also possesses an uncertainty: the particle has passed through the slit of breadth *d* and not through a single point of it. Instead of using *d,* we denote the uncertainty in the position of the particle by the more meaningful symbol Δx, and likewise the uncertainty in the velocity by Δv. The uncertainty in the momentum is then $\Delta p = m\Delta v$. Let us now multiply the uncertainties in position and momentum together. The first of these is *d* and the second is:

$$\Delta v \sim \frac{2(ac)v}{ab} = \frac{v\lambda}{d} = \frac{v}{d}\left(\frac{h}{mv}\right) = \frac{h}{dm} \text{ *}$$

The variables cancel on multiplication and we obtain a relationship that is fundamental to quantum mechanics:

$$\Delta p \Delta x \sim h **$$

This means that the product of uncertainties in momentum and position is equal to Planck's constant. The more precisely the coordinate is defined, i.e., the smaller is Δx, the less precisely can the momentum be given, since Δp is inversely proportional to Δx. Conversely, the more precisely the mo-

---

* Factor 2 allows for the fact that the deviation may be up or down.
** Using advanced mathematics we can show that the exact statement of the uncertainty principle is:

$$\Delta p \Delta x \geq \tfrac{1}{2}h/2\pi$$

mentum is defined, the worse the definition of the particle's position is.

We shall constantly encounter this fact in all experiments on diffraction, since it is impossible to force a wave to be propagated with the same precision as that with which a particle moves. Bohr and Heisenberg analyzed a number of thought-experiments (*gedanken*-experiments) in which the co-ordinate of a particle and its momentum could be defined with the greatest possible precision (aside from instrumental errors). It was found that in all cases these two quantities could not be physically determined (i.e., exactly measured) at the same time. Measurement, if it could be free from experimental errors, is a physical determination of a quantity, since it reveals the properties of the objects of measurement and not of the measuring systems. Objects are also determined solely through measurement in classical physics.

Let us recall a well-known fact from the history of physics. For a very long time inventors tried to construct, or at least to design, a perpetual motion machine, i.e., an imaginary machine that would do useful work without an external supply of energy. Peter the Great of Russia was so interested in this idea that he founded an academy especially for this research.* However, if we even without knowing the general principle of the conservation of energy analyze any actual design of a perpetual motion machine, we can always find a mistake in it. All these unsuccessful designs or imaginary experiments have led physicists to the conclusion that a perpetual motion machine simply cannot be constructed. This assertion is one way of expressing the conservation of energy principle.

Similarly, the imaginary experiments on the measurement of position and momentum led Bohr and Heisenberg to another conclusion, no less fundamental to physics: the position and the momentum of a particle do not exist simultaneously as precisely definable quantities. This is known as the

* See V. L. Kirpichev; *Besedy o mekhanike* (Discussions on mechanics), Gostekhizdat, 1951, p. 289.

uncertainty principle. It is impossible even in principle to devise a procedure that would bring about the precise *determination,* i.e., *measurement* of both position and momentum. This is not a subjective defect in the experimenters, but an objective law of nature.

For those who wish to refute the uncertainty principle by means of imaginary experiments, the sad fate of the inventors of perpetual motion machines is waiting. Einstein tried to devise such an experiment, but even he, of course, could not prove stronger than nature. This example must now serve as a cautionary tale for critics of the uncertainty principle who are still to be found among people interested in physics and even among a small number of physicists.

The uncertainty principle in no way denies the existence of momentum and position as precise physical quantities; it merely asserts that they cannot exist simultaneously as precise quantities. Each of them separately may be measured or given with as much precision as desired.

This assertion contains a denial of deep-rooted physical concepts. In speaking of the trajectory of a particle, we understand that at every instant of time it has a definite position and velocity (or momentum). The uncertainty principle renders this assertion meaningless, of course, only as far as microscopic particles are concerned. For macroscopic particles, Planck's constant on the right-hand side of the uncertainty relationship is a very small quantity, and consequently the velocity and position may be defined simultaneously for macroscopic particles with practically any necessary degree of precision; i.e., the trajectory concept is always valid in practice for macroscopic particles.

Thus quantum mechanics provides its own special concept of mechanical motion without trajectories. The analysis of motion along trajectories makes it possible to predict future data uniquely in terms of the past. In quantum mechanics, this prediction has a probabilistic character. Of course, this does not totally deny the laws of motion; it simply means that the laws of quantum mechanics give us the probability of obtaining different values of various quantities and do not refer to the quantities themselves. We may describe the probability that an electron will strike this or that point of a photographic plate, but cannot in principle predict which point it will actually strike.

Hence, unlike the classical laws of motion, the quantum-mechanical laws of motion incorporate the concept of probability, and this is not connected with imperfections in the apparatus, but rests in the nature of things.

Experiment shows that the probability distribution for electrons striking a photographic plate obeys the same laws as those for the diffraction of electromagnetic waves. We have already mentioned that the diffraction of electrons is completely independent of the intensity of the electron beam and occurs even when the electrons pass through the crystal practically one by one. However, electromagnetic waves are diffracted because a wave has different phases on different planes of an atomic lattice. Consequently, the electron also must have different phases on different planes. We recall that to obtain the diffraction of electromagnetic waves, light from a single source must be used—only then does the phase of the wave have a definite value on each plane. We called this a *coherent* wave. In this sense every electron is coherent with itself alone, just as every source of light is.

Coherent waves can cancel each other out when their phases are opposite; but the probabilities of an electron striking this or that point of the plate cannot cancel each other, for they are positive by definition. In the same way, in the case of diffraction of light, the intensities do not cancel each other out, since they are also essentially positive. Only the electromagnetic field strengths, i.e., the amplitudes of the waves, may be added or subtracted. Similarly, in the case of electrons, the amplitudes of the probabilities of finding an electron at a given point of space may cancel each other out. Only the *amplitudes* and not the probabilities can possess *wave* properties. Hence the motion of an electron in a crystal is described by a *wave* function similar to the electromagnetic wave in the propagation of light. The intensity is equal to the square of the amplitude of the electromagnetic oscillations; similarly, the probability of finding an electron at this or that point of space is equal the square of the amplitude of the wave function describing its motion.

Therefore, we may answer the direct question: what oscillates during the motion of an electron? The answer is that the amplitude of the probability of finding it at a given point of space oscillates. This amplitude has the properties of a wave.

The probability concept is not completely foreign even to classical or Newtonian mechanics. Let us begin with an example taken from everyday life and then show that in quantum mechanics probability, being connected with the very nature of things, goes far more deeply.

It is well known that when one is shooting at a target, bullets do not strike the same point twice. The better the marksman the closer the shots, but there is always some scatter. Even with perfect aim there would still be scatter, for example, caused by slight differences in the powder charges.

Even a poor marksman can sometimes hit the bull's-eye by chance—but it is extremely unlikely that he will hit the bull's-eye five times in succession. The scatter of the shots on the target reveals the skill of the marksman or, in other words, the probability that he will hit the mark. For a sufficiently great number of shots we could obtain a smooth curve of the distribution of the impact probabilities on the target.

In classical mechanics the probability concept is introduced because it is impossible to reproduce initial conditions of motion perfectly. This is the basis of the game of "heads or tails," which is frequently used to explain the most important propositions of probability theory.

The concept of probability *amplitude* cannot arise in classical mechanics: if we do not know the trajectory of a particle precisely, we can calculate only the probability of its passing through this or that point of space, e.g., the probability of hitting the bull's-eye. In quantum physics, the matter is quite different—motion does not take place along trajectories, just as the propagation of light in diffraction does not correspond to any light rays. We cannot describe the trajectory of an electron in a crystal simply because it does not exist. Here we must use the concept of probability amplitude.

Another concept not appearing in classical mechanics is that of the phase of a wave function. Of course, only the phase *differences* are revealed by the diffraction phenomena in the case of scattering by different lattice planes. Since the final diffraction pattern is completely independent of whether the electrons pass through the crystal all at once or one at a time, we have to recognize that the wave function of an individual electron possesses a phase. Each electron in this experiment is coherent with itself, like the light wave in the diffraction experiment, and hence the pattern obtained on the photographic plate does not in the least recall the distribution curve for bullets on a target. The better the definition of the initial conditions of motion of the electrons and the more ideal the crystal, the sharper and clearer is the diffraction pattern.

It is not the electron itself that has a wave-like character but only the amplitude of the probability of finding it at some point in space. In this sense it is more correct to speak of the wave-like character of *motion,* for diffraction phenomena are also observed in the motion of other atomic particles.

Why is there no diffraction in the case of the motion of ordinary bodies, such as bullets, stones and missiles? We have seen that the wavelength is inversely proportional to the mass of the particle. If the mass of the particle is 1 g and its velocity is only 1 cm/sec, then by the fundamental formula $\lambda = h/mv$, the wavelength is $\lambda = 6.6 \times 10^{-27}$ cm. It is inconceivable, however, that any position could be specified with such enormous precision. Even the radius of an atom is of the order of

10^{-8} cm. It follows that the laws of wave mechanics simply have no effect on the motion of such macroscopic bodies, but it goes without saying that classical mechanics may be applied to them. Atomic particles, especially electrons, may be called *microscopic* bodies. Classical mechanics may often be applied to them too. For example, the motion of an electron in a television picture tube is classical.

In an ordinary optical microscope, the limit of resolution is determined by the wavelength of light, for objects much smaller than this cannot be observed. Electrons with energy of 20,000 eV have a wavelength of 10^{-9} cm. This is 100,000 times smaller than that of visible light, and hence an electron microscope may be used to observe and photograph objects 100,000 times smaller than an optical microscope can.

As we have already seen, the concept of a classical trajectory is not always applicable to the motion of electrons. In the atomic, microscopic region everything is determined by the laws of wave mechanics.

The laws of quantum mechanics contain the concept of probability, or more precisely, the probability amplitude; and this is not at all connected with our subjective lack of knowledge of the initial conditions of motion. As a precise physical concept, a trajectory has no physical existence in relation to microparticles.

The quantum laws of motion do not negate the classical laws; they only impose a quantitative limit on their applicability. This limit is given by the uncertainty relationship, which still employs classical concepts of position and momentum. So long as Δp and Δx are small in comparison with p and x, which characterize a given actual motion along a trajectory, the classical laws of motion may be applied; but if the uncertainties in these quantities equal or exceed the quantities themselves, the quantum laws are necessary. Unlike the classical laws, these predict the results of experiments not uniquely but in probability form.

We also note that quantum mechanics cannot answer at all

the question of what an electron is or what is its structure. This is the concern of the theory of elementary particles—a science that is far from complete. The name mechanics underlines the fact that we are studying specific laws of motion and not the nature of moving objects. Similarly, classical mechanics is concerned with the motion of planets around the sun but not with the planets' composition or internal structure. Quantum mechanics explains the motions of electrons about the nucleus of an atom on the basis, and solely on the basis, of the properties of nuclei and electrons that are important in a given actual case. Quantum mechanics solves this problem as completely as classical mechanics solves the fundamental problem of astronomy.

In this sense quantum and classical mechanics are complete to the same degree. The equations of classical mechanics can be obtained "in the limit" from the quantum equations simply by allowing Planck's constant h to tend to zero. (More precisely, the wavelength associated with the motion becomes infinitely small in comparison with the region in which the motion takes place. However, the wavelength is directly proportional to Planck's constant so that, formally, this is equivalent to h tending to zero.) The uncertainties Δp and Δx become, so to speak, disconnected, and may be made as small as desired independently of each other. Therefore the trajectory concept becomes valid.

When a theory of elementary particles is finally developed, it will no doubt change and extend the present-day concept of motion in quantum mechanics, but it will have to be retained as a limiting case. We may be sure of this in advance, since quantum mechanics gives a correct and consistent description of a definite range of natural phenomena. Since the laws governing these phenomena cannot change, nor internal consistency become inconsistent, quantum mechanics will always remain correct in its own range of application, just as classical mechanics has remained applicable in its own domain even after the advent of quantum mechanics; but when the theory of elementary particles is established, we shall also have to take into account the theory of relativity (see Chapter Eight).

The uncertainty principle contains an assertion that is considerably more general than is evident from the uncertainty relationship, $\Delta p \Delta x = h$ for the specific quantities p and x. To show this, let us obtain similar relationships for another pair of variables. We observe first of all that the components of momentum and position to which the uncertainty relationship refers must be taken in the same direction. They do not refer to variables taken in mutually perpendicular directions. These components may be defined simultaneously with any desired degree of precision.

Let us now recall the definition of angular momentum from mechanics. Let the motion take place in a given plane (Fig. 15) and consider an axis perpendicular to the plane. The linear momentum of the particle is represented by a vector lying in the plane. Angular momentum is defined as the product of the linear momentum by the length of the perpendicular drawn from the point where the axis cuts the plane to the vector p. In mechanics we often use rotational motion or, in general, motion about a center of force. In fact it turns out that if the force acts along a line drawn from the center to the particle (this holds good for the force of gravity and for electrostatic forces), then angular momentum is constant. In

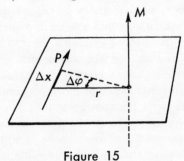

Figure 15

this case we must draw the axis perpendicular to the plane through the center of force. Thus in Figure 15 the axis can pass through the nucleus of an atom.

The proof of the law of conservation of angular momentum may be found in textbooks on mechanics. We ought not to formulate it in the same way, since we are considering motion according to quantum-mechanical laws, i.e., motion without trajectories. However, there is remarkable agreement between the two systems; if a certain quantity is conserved in classical motion, then it is also conserved in quantum motion. Of course, this assertion is limited somewhat by the uncertainty principle; for only quantities that can coexist simultaneously can be conserved simultaneously. The fact that the same conservation laws hold in both classical and quantum mechanics is of fundamental importance. This is called the correspondence principle, for it allows us to write down quantum equations of motion if we know the form of the classical equations for a given mechanical system.

Let us now return to the angular momentum. Denoting momentum as usual by p and the perpendicular distance from the axis by r, we have, by definition, that the angular momentum $M = pr$. Since p and r are perpendicular, they may be defined simultaneously; but if we speak of the displacement of the particle along a trajectory, then in accordance with the uncertainty principle, it can be defined only with an uncertainty Δx. It is clear from the diagram that $\Delta x = r\Delta\phi$ where the azimuth ϕ is the angle that, together with the distance from the axis, gives the position of the particle on the plane (we are not obliged to use Cartesian coordinates x and y).

From the uncertainty relationship we have $\Delta p \Delta x = h$, but since $\Delta x = r\Delta\phi$, we have $\Delta p \cdot r\Delta\phi = h$. This may be rewritten $\Delta (rp) \cdot \Delta\phi = h$ since r is perpendicular to p. Remembering the definition of angular momentum, we obtain the uncertainty relationship for the angular momentum and the azimuth angle: $\Delta M \Delta\phi = h$. We see that the angular momentum cannot exist as a precise quantity simultaneously with the azimuth angle. If, for example, the angular momentum is known precisely (and is conserved since the force is central), then the position of the particle in its orbit is completely undefined. We shall often return to this point.

Let us now consider how we are to understand the law of conservation of energy in the light of the uncertainty principle. As we know, the energy consists of two parts, kinetic and potential. The kinetic energy of a particle depends on its velocity, and the potential energy on its position. For example, the potential energy of a particle in a gravitational field is proportional to the height to which it is raised. Similar expressions may also be obtained for an electrostatic field.

However, a position coordinate and the corresponding velocity do not exist simultaneously. Does this mean that the uncertainty principle revokes the law of conservation of energy? Not at all, for we have already said that the conservation laws of classical and quantum mechanics are the same. The difference is that in quantum mechanics the energy of a particle cannot be divided exactly into kinetic and potential energies. Only the total energy has a precise meaning and only the total energy is conserved. The conservation conditions are exactly the same as in classical mechanics: no work may be done on the system by external forces. Since the energy is conserved, such systems are said to be *conservative*. In particular, energy is conserved in a closed system, i.e., one that does not interact with surrounding systems.

3 Quantum laws of motion

Wave motions under extremely diverse conditions have much in common. This allows us to explain many cases of atomic particle motion if not quantitatively, at least qualitatively with the aid of obvious optical and acoustic analogies.

We must here consider in detail, first of all, the behavior of a wave on the boundary between two media. Figure 2 shows the path of rays refracted from such a boundary. The angle between the ray and the normal to the boundary is smaller in the denser medium. If we now allow the angle of incidence (i.e., the angle to the normal) to increase until it reaches 90°, the refracted ray will also make a larger angle with the normal, although it will always be less than 90°. The angle corresponding to 90° incidence is called the angle of total internal reflection. In fact, a ray moving in the reverse direction, i.e., from the denser medium, at an angle greater than the angle of total internal reflection, will not be able to penetrate the optically rarer medium at all, and will be totally reflected back into the denser medium. It is for this reason that air bubbles in water appear silvery from a certain angle. Total internal reflection is also used in prismatic binoculars. Because of reflection from the internal surfaces of special prisms, the image appears "right side up" instead of inverted.

The phenomenon of total internal reflection may be equally

well explained by either the wave or the corpuscular theory. Both lead to the same law of refraction.

However, as an example, here is one complication that cannot be explained from the corpuscular point of view. Let us assume that the rarer medium is totally enclosed inside the denser medium and is in the form of a very thin layer with approximately the thickness of a single wavelength. In this case the reflection from the layer will cease to be total even when it should be according to the laws of geometric optics. The explanation is that the waves still penetrate a little into the rarer medium, even when they strike it at an angle greater than the angle of total internal reflection. In this case the waves are very rapidly attenuated in the rarer medium and, most important, do not carry any energy very far into it. If the optically rarer medium is sufficiently thick, all the energy will be reflected back into the denser medium (total reflection); but when the rarer medium takes the form of a thin layer, the wave, not being completely attenuated in it, is partially transmitted into the denser medium. The denser medium "picks up" the wave and carries it further. The wave is propagated in it without attenuation. Thus when a wave strikes a thin layer of the optically rarer medium, the reflection ceases to be total. Of course, ray optics cannot explain this: a ray is reflected from the geometric surface of the medium, and "knows" nothing about what happens beyond the surface. Once again we discover that the wave nature of light is demonstrated during propagation in a region comparable with a wavelength, in this case—in a thin layer.

This case, however, is essentially different from diffraction since, in addition to ordinary traveling waves, there is also an attenuated wave in the layer (waves that pass through a slit in a screen are not attenuated). Figure 9 shows a wave that is not attenuated in space; all its crests are of the same height. Figures 16 and 17 show two types of attenuated wave. In the first the oscillations are still preserved, but in the second they are eliminated completely. This depends on the attenuating

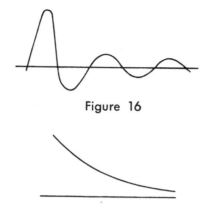

Figure 16

Figure 17

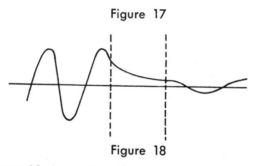

Figure 18

force. Figure 18 shows the typical course of a wave that is partly attenuated in a layer, and then transmitted into the denser medium where it is not attenuated. In this case there is a considerable decrease in the height of the crests.

We must note one detail in the diagram. All three sections of the wave are smoothly joined without any discontinuity. The slopes on both sides of the point where they join are the same.

This is best interpreted with the example of a sound wave. Since the fundamental laws of wave motion are the same we may choose as an analogy the case that is the easiest to study. An acoustic analogy will be suitable for our purpose because, among other reasons, phenomena such as total internal reflection also occur in sound waves. We must first explain the physical meaning of the slope of the wave in this case. We assume that the wave represents a variation of pressure, which is a maximum on the crests and a minimum in the troughs. The greatest drop in pressure occurs halfway between crest and trough. If a curve were constructed for the distribution of the velocity of the air, at the points of maximum and minimum pressure it would be zero, and where the pressure drop was greatest it would be a maximum. In other words, the velocity curve has the same shape as the pressure curve, but is displaced through a quarter of a wavelength (Fig. 9). At every point the velocity is defined simply as the slope of the pressure curve; but the velocity of matter cannot suffer a discontinuity on the boundary between two media, for if it did, matter from the first medium would penetrate into the second, which is impossible. The velocity curves must therefore join smoothly. By Newton's third law there can be no pressure jump on the boundary: action must equal reaction. The velocity cannot approach the boundary with a different slope on either side, since that would entail a discontinuity in the velocity.

The same principle can be justified for waves of probability amplitude. We chose a sound wave for clarity: the mathematical quantities for which continuity has been established have a simple physical interpretation in the case of sound, but the result will be the same.

We have already spoken of the principle of correspondence between classical and quantum mechanics. Any concept of classical mechanics may be transferred into quantum mechanics if it does not conflict with the uncertainty principle. In particular, the concept of position has a meaning, although not, of course, at the same time as momentum. It follows that the concept of potential energy is valid, provided that kinetic energy is left undefined—the two cannot exist simultaneously for a given state of a particle.

For simplicity we shall consider motion in one dimension, since the potential energy then depends on a single coordinate. What obvious meaning can be given to potential energy in the wave picture, i.e., if we use the probability amplitude, or the wave function? We are no longer bound to consider a given position coordinate as the coordinate of the particle itself—it is only the argument of the wave function, the square of which determines the possibility of finding the particle at a given point.

Potential energy that varies in space will correspond to a varying index of refraction. This assertion may be readily verified. The sum of potential and kinetic energies is the total energy, which is constant. Consequently, the greater the potential energy for a given total energy, the smaller will be the kinetic energy. And the smaller the kinetic energy, the smaller the velocity of the particle. As we have seen, since the wavelength is inversely proportional to velocity, the motion of the particle in a region with varying potential energy corresponds to wave propagation in an inhomogeneous medium where the wavelength varies. This in turn means that the index of refraction varies from point to point. If we call the total energy E and the potential energy U, then the kinetic energy equals $E - U$. On the other hand, the kinetic energy is $mv^2/2$, from which $v = \sqrt{2(E - U)/m}$ and the wavelength is $\lambda = h/mv = h/\sqrt{2m(E - U)}$. A variable depending on a single coordinate can be conveniently plotted on a graph, as can also be done in the case of potential energy. Let us consider some typical examples.

1. *Uniform field of force.* The gravitational field on the surface of the earth and the electric field in a plane capacitor are examples of uniform fields of force. We know that potential energy is defined as the work that must be done to bring a body to a given point. In the case of a constant force the work is simply the product of the force and the distance traveled along the direction of the force, so that the potential energy in a constant uniform field is proportional to the path

length, i.e., to the position coordinate. The graph of this relationship is, as is well known, a straight line whose slope is clearly equal to the force, because it is numerically equal to the work done per unit path length.

2. *Elastic force.* This is the name given to a force that is proportional to the distance of the body on which the force acts from the position of equilibrium. The force in a stretched spring may serve as an example: the greater the extension, the greater the force. In quantum theory we do not encounter bodies such as springs, but we see at once from the potential energy curve that elastic forces are not restricted to springs. Let us first draw the graph of the force as a function of the distance. Since these are proportional quantities, the graph will be a straight line (Fig. 19), but this is still not what we need. We must calculate the work required to displace a particle from the origin O to some other position, for example, the point A. It is now impossible to assert, as in the previous case, that the work is simply equal to the product of force times distance, since the force is different at different points of the path. If the force were the same everywhere, the work would be equal to the area of the rectangle OB_1BA. In the present case, as may be seen directly from the sketch, it is only half as great, i.e., it is equal to the area of the triangle OBA. The length AB is proportional to the OA, and since the area

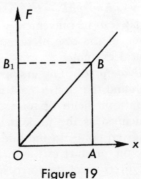

Figure 19

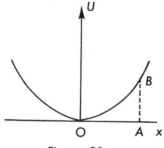

Figure 20

equals $\frac{1}{2} OA \cdot AB$, it is proportional to the square of OA. The graph of the latter relationship is shown in Figure 20, where the curve is drawn for displacements from O on either side of the origin.

At O (or the position of equilibrium) there is no force on the particle. When the particle is displaced, a force acts upon it, which tends to restore it to O, so that the equilibrium at this point is stable. We may now clarify the meaning of an elastic force: it is the force acting on a particle near the position of stable equilibrium. If, for example, an atom in equilibrium in a molecule is displaced, an elastic force acts upon it. For sufficiently great displacements, the force is no longer proportional to the displacement, and the potential energy curve is no longer as shown in Figure 20. However, it is often sufficient to consider only small displacements.

3. *Electrostatic force, inversely proportional to the square of the distance.* Here again the work cannot be taken as equal to the product of force and distance, since the force is variable. A simple construction such as that of Figure 19 is of no help; but we can find the expression for the potential energy without higher mathematics. At a distance r the force equals a/r^2 (where a is a constant of proportionality) and at a distance $r + \Delta r$ it is $a/(r + \Delta r)^2$. If Δr is small, we can replace both values of the force by their geometric mean $a/r(r + \Delta r)$, i.e., we take the force to be approximately constant in the in-

terval Δr, and so the work done in Δr equals $a\Delta r/r(r + \Delta r)$, which is equal to $(a/r) - a/(r + \Delta r)$. We now consider the next interval between $r + \Delta r$ and $r + 2\Delta r$. Here the work equals $a/(r + \Delta r) - a/(r + 2\Delta r)$. Adding up the work done in the intervals $(r,\ r + \Delta r)$ and $(r + \Delta r,\ r + 2\Delta r)$, we see that intermediate term $a/(r + \Delta r)$ disappears. The same will happen if we take another interval, and so on. Finally, the work equals the difference in the values of a/r at the ends of the path. If the potential energy is defined as the work done in transferring the particle from infinity to a given point, then at infinity the term $a/(r = \infty)$ will vanish, and we will be left with only a/r. The graph of this relationship is given in Figure 21.

Since the force in the given case is attractive (a is negative), it acts in the direction of decreasing distance, i.e., against the direction of r, and hence the potential energy curve lies entirely below the r axis. For repulsive forces, which obey the inverse square law (e.g., like charges), the curve will lie entirely above the r axis.

The form of the dependence of potential energy on distance could be guessed in an extremely simple way. Since the force is inversely proportional to the square of the distance, and the dimensions of work are equal to the dimensions of force

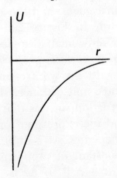

Figure 21

multiplied by length, we may conclude that the potential energy is inversely proportional to the first power of the distance. However, it is impossible to prove by this means that the constant coefficient—in this case a—is the same for the force and for the work. Indeed, for an elastic force, the constant coefficient in the potential energy was smaller by a factor of 2, although the dimensions were the same. Hence for a force inversely proportional to the square of the distance we needed a stricter derivation.

The potential energy curve will allow us to make further deductions more easily, and the reader must understand their significance very clearly. Figure 20 gives a plot of the work that must be done to displace a particle from the origin to a given point, and Figure 21 plots the work of transferring the particle from infinity to the given point. We should add that tests (educational, not physical) show that 90 percent of the difficulty in understanding the concepts of quantum mechanics arise from an insufficient grasp of elementary laws of mechanics, and only 10 percent is connected with the new ideas.

Quantum mechanics is a continuation of classical mechanics. This does not mean of course that it could be logically deduced from Newton's laws of motion. An element of conjecture must always exist in the creation of new theories. Thus, 3 years before the diffraction of electrons was demonstrated experimentally, Louis de Broglie proposed that the motion of electrons should exhibit wave properties. Developing de Broglie's idea, Schrödinger obtained an equation for the wave function and thus created the mathematical apparatus of quantum mechanics. Working completely independently, Heisenberg found another, equally valuable form of quantum mechanics. Only later was direct experimental confirmation obtained. This does not mean that de Broglie, Schrödinger and Heisenberg had no experimental basis for their work. On the contrary, an enormous quantity of experimental material had already been accumulated that could not be explained by classical theory.

However, quantum theory in its old primitive form did not explain the diffraction of light. Seeking a solution for this difficulty, de Broglie proposed a synthesis of the corpuscular and wave representations.

We must always remember that intuition is fruitful only when actual laws of nature are discovered with its aid. For one correct guess there are innumerable wrong ones, generally made by people wishing to teach without bothering to learn.

Let us now return to the potential energy curves. The examples just considered (the second and especially the third) are extremely important in quantum mechanics, but it is impossible to obtain deductions from them by simple means without higher mathematics. We shall, therefore, consider one more curve, which is not encountered in reality, but which helps us to understand all the fundamental laws of motion in quantum mechanics.

4. *Box with impenetrable walls.* The "box" that we shall consider is one-dimensional in form, i.e., a straight line along which a particle can move freely without performing work or having work done on it by external forces. This corresponds to the flat bottom of a box. When moving along the bottom of the box the particle does not change its potential energy. How may we define the inpenetrability of the walls physically? We must assume that the work needed to penetrate the wall, however slightly, is infinite; but we know that the work done on the particle and the potential energy can be represented by the same curve, which must rise vertically up at the walls of the box. The potential energy curve for an elastic force also tends to infinity, but gradually. In the latter case, infinite work must be done to remove the particle an infinite distance from the origin. In the case of the box, infinite work is required to remove the particle even the smallest distance beyond the limits of the box (Fig. 22a). We can now establish what the curve must look like if by doing a *finite* amount of work we can penetrate beyond the wall. The graph

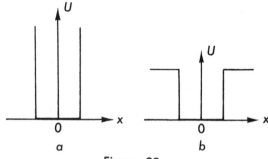

Figure 22

representing this amount of work will rise vertically at the boundary of the box, and then become horizontal again, since no more work is necessary for further displacement (Fig. 22b).

Our knowledge is now sufficient to consider all the more important cases of motion of a quantum particle. We shall have to seek the wave function according to the form of the potential energy curve. This is one of the fundamental problems of quantum mechanics, just as finding the trajectory from the form of the potential energy is a fundamental problem of classical mechanics. The wave function does not, of course, replace the trajectory in any way; we are not dealing with physical waves but with probability amplitudes.

In Figures 19-22, the total energy could be plotted together with the potential energy. The total energy has a direct meaning as a mechanical quantity; potential energy is only needed for finding the wave function. The total energy is conserved; i.e., being the same at all points it has a graph with the simplest possible form: a straight horizontal line.

How far can this line be continued? Let us take, for example, Figure 22b. We assume that the total energy is less than the depth of the "potential well," i.e., less than the work needed to get the particle out of the well. In classical mechanics the particle cannot get out of the well at all: the entire region of classical motion lies between the points *A* and *B* (Fig. 23). To

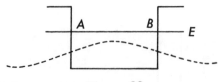

Figure 23

the left of A and to the right of B the total energy is less than the depth of the potential well. Hence outside the well the kinetic energy is a negative quantity. However, this is impossible—kinetic energy is of course half the product of the mass (a positive quantity) by the square of the velocity (also positive). Negative kinetic energy would correspond to an imaginary velocity that, of course, the particle cannot have. Classical motion with total energy less than the depth of the potential well is thus limited by the size of the well, and the particle must remain in the well.

In quantum mechanics the total energy is well defined, but because of the uncertainty principle, the potential and kinetic energies are not separately well defined; these quantities cannot exist simultaneously.*

This is connected with the fact that position and velocity cannot be simultaneously defined, so that it is impossible to assert that to the left of A or to the right of B or anywhere else at all, the particle has any given velocity. The limitation imposed by classical mechanics is thus removed: a particle may perfectly well appear in a classically forbidden region.

In other words, the wave function for the particle does not become zero immediately beyond the limits of the well—there is a finite probability of finding the particle there too. If we use the wave analogy as we have done before, then here we must draw a parallel with total internal reflection. We have already said that a particle with total energy E corresponds

* We note that in quantum mechanics it would be possible to define the mean values of the potential and kinetic energies for the whole region of motion where the wave function is not zero. These mean values do exist simultaneously and satisfy the same relationships as in classical mechanics.

to the de Broglie wavelength $\lambda = h/mv = h/\sqrt{2mE}$ in the well where $U = 0$, and $\lambda = h/\sqrt{2m(E - U)}$ outside the well. However, since $U > E$ the latter quantity is imaginary, which turns out to correspond to the attenuation of the wave as in Figure 17. A light wave is similarly attenuated in the optically rarer medium in the case of total internal reflection. Within the framework of ray optics, which corresponds to classical mechanics, the ray of light does not penetrate the optically rarer medium if the angle of incidence is greater than the angle of total internal reflection. The laws of wave optics temper this categorical prohibition. Instead, we find that an attenuated wave may still be propagated in the forbidden region of classical mechanics. It must be emphasized that this analogy with optics is based only on the similarity between the laws of wave motion; there is no real physical similarity. In the case of total internal reflection of light we have damped oscillations. On the other hand, the wave function in the classically forbidden region falls off smoothly (cf. Figs. 17 and 23).

The analogy with the general laws of wave motion may nevertheless be taken further. At the beginning of the chapter it was shown that waves meet smoothly at any boundary separating media—one passes into the other without jump or break. The wave function is shown in Figure 23 by a dotted line. For a given total energy, the deeper the well, the faster the function is attenuated outside it. In the limiting case of an infinitely deep well or "box," such as in Figure 22a, the function simply vanishes on the boundary. In other words, even a quantum particle cannot get out in this case.

Let us consider this very simple case first. It shows that in the well, the energy of the particle is far from arbitrary. We know that an oscillating quantity is zero when the phase of the wave equals 0, π, 2π, etc. Hence if the wave function becomes zero at the boundary, the length of the well must be either half the de Broglie wavelength, or a whole wavelength, or one-and-a-half wavelengths, or two wavelengths, i.e., any integral number of half wavelengths. Let us denote this integer by n. The length of the box must therefore be $a = \frac{1}{2}n\lambda$, but since $\lambda = h/\sqrt{2mE}$, the energy of the particle in the box must be equal to one of the values $E_n = n^2h^2/8ma^2$ and can take no other values.

This result is of fundamental importance. It shows that the energy may not always be a continuous entity as in classical mechanics. This is called the *quantization of energy** and the values assumed are called energy levels, since all the possible values may be arranged one above the other as levels.

If the well is of finite depth, as in Figure 22b, the position in principle does not change. As long as the total energy is less than the depth of the well, the wave function must join up smoothly on both boundaries with an attenuated curve of the form shown in Figure 17. Although the length of the well no longer has to be a whole number of half waves (the amplitude is not zero at the boundaries of the well), it is clear that a smooth connection cannot be obtained for every wavelength. The heights and slopes of the curve must be the same on either side of the boundary. These so-called boundary conditions will also restrict the energy E to certain values E_n; but these are not expressed so simply in terms of n as in the case of an infinitely deep well. What is still more important is that for a well of finite depth the number of energy levels is also finite. The last of these levels lies a little way below the upper boundary of the well.

When the energy of the particle is greater than the depth of the well, the position changes considerably. Here the wave function outside the well is also not attenuated, since there too $E > U$, but a smooth connection of this function with the function inside the well is possible for any value of the energy. An unattenuated wave line, of course, may start with any slope, so that the wave function inside the well may be con-

* The Latin word *quantum* means "amount." A system with quantized energy may receive or give up only definite amounts, *quanta,* of energy corresponding to the difference between the possible levels. Hence the term "quantum mechanics" is used.

nected with the function outside for any value of the energy. It follows that the energy in this case does not assume a number of discrete values, but varies continuously as in classical mechanics.

It is easy to observe the basic difference between these two cases. When the energy is less than the depth of the well, the probability that the particle will be very far from the well is extremely small, and tends to zero in the limit of very great distances. Here the wave function is attenuated. This means that the particle cannot leave the well completely. Classically, it can move only within the limits of the well, while in quantum theory it can get out of the well, but only "temporarily." Hence we say that a quantum particle is *bound* to the well, or that it is in the *bound state*. It turns out that only bound states are quantized. When the energy lies above the upper boundary of the well, the wave function outside the well is not attenuated, and the probability of a particle moving away to an infinite distance is now certainly not zero. This means, however, that it must go out of the well and not return to it. Classically, this motion corresponds to an unbound state, the energy of which varies continuously.

The assertion expressed here does not refer only to "square" wells of the form shown in Figure 22a, b. The bound state allows only a number of discrete values of the total energy, but the free state allows a continuous range of values. The set of all possible values of the energy of a given system is called its *energy spectrum*. The bound state has, as we say, a discrete spectrum, and the free state has a continuous spectrum. This terminology bears some relation to the optical spectrum, which we shall discuss later.

Interestingly, the term "spectrum" was applied to mathematical problems of wave motion by mathematicians long before the creation of quantum mechanics. The well-known external resemblance between the line spectrum observed in optics and the set of points or dashes representing a discrete sequence of numbers clearly helped to prompt this usage.

There are also wells in which the particle has only bound states. We have already considered a very simple example—an infinitely deep rectangular well. Another example is the potential well corresponding to an elastic force. The potential energy curve may in principle go as high as we please, while the total energy cannot be greater than the potential energy everywhere. A horizontal line must intersect the potential energy curve somewhere. Hence here too we must obtain only discrete energy levels. Unlike the case of an infinitely deep rectangular well, the wave function will not become zero at the points where the line representing the total energy cuts the potential energy curve, but a particle with finite energy will not be able to get more than a limited distance away from the well.

The energy spectrum in this case has an exceptionally simple form, which consists of an infinite number of equidistant levels (Fig. 24). The distance between the levels may be obtained as follows. Let us forget quantum theory for the moment. An elastic force gives rise to simple harmonic oscillation of a particle with frequency v. We shall borrow this characteristic of oscillatory motion from classical mechanics, although no harmonic oscillations occur in the quantum case. The distance between the quantum levels then equals hv, and the energy of the lowest level is $hv/2$. Hence the energy levels are given by $E_n = (n + \frac{1}{2})hv$ where n is an integer.

Why does the lowest or *ground state,* as it is called, not lie at the bottom of the well; i.e., why is the ground state energy not equal to zero? This is easy to understand from the uncertainty principle. With strictly zero energy it would have strictly zero momentum. The uncertainty of position would then be infinitely great; i.e., the particle could be at any distance from the well; but it is bound to the well. Hence both the position and the momentum of the particle in the ground state as in all the others are somewhat smeared, although least of all in the ground state (cf. the lowest level in Fig. 24). In the ground state of a quantum oscillatory motion, the uncertainties of position and momentum are the least possible and are half as

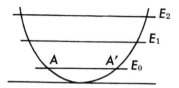

Figure 24

great as in the case of free motion. To make this more precise, the energy of a particle is, classically,

$$E = \tfrac{1}{2}mv^2 + \tfrac{1}{2}kx^2$$

$$= \frac{1}{2}\frac{p^2}{m} + \frac{1}{2}kx^2$$

Now, in the ground state, the energy and momentum are related by the uncertainty relation

$$px = \frac{1}{2}\frac{h}{2\pi}$$

Thus,
$$E = \frac{1}{4}\left(\frac{h}{2\pi}\right)^2 \frac{1}{2}\frac{1}{m}\frac{1}{x^2} + \frac{1}{2}kx^2$$

This is illustrated in Figure 25.

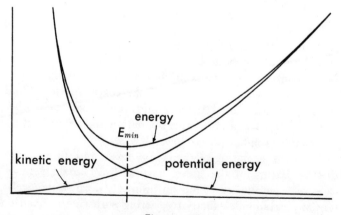

Figure 25

It is clear that the minimum energy occurs when

$$\frac{1}{2} kx^2 = \frac{1}{4} \left(\frac{h}{2\pi}\right)^2 \frac{1}{2} \frac{1}{m} \frac{1}{x^2}$$

$$x^2 = \frac{1}{2} \frac{h}{2\pi} \frac{1}{\sqrt{km}}$$

or $$E = \frac{1}{4} \left(\frac{h}{2\pi}\right)^2 \frac{1}{2} \frac{1}{m} \frac{\sqrt{km}}{\frac{1}{2} \frac{h}{2\pi}} + \frac{1}{2} k \frac{1}{2} \frac{h}{2\pi} \frac{1}{\sqrt{km}} = \frac{1}{2} \frac{h}{2\pi} \sqrt{\frac{k}{m}}$$

The classical frequency of oscillation is given by

$$\nu = \frac{1}{2\pi} \sqrt{\frac{k}{m}}$$

$$Eg = \tfrac{1}{2}h\nu$$

Eg is the minimum energy consistent with the uncertainty principle.

We have already indicated that atoms in a molecule are bound by forces resembling elastic forces. The result obtained here, therefore, has an immediate application to the energy of molecular oscillations even though molecules cannot be represented by infinitely deep wells. There is always a finite energy of dissociation of molecules into atoms.

Under these conditions the potential energy curve resembles that of Figure 22b, but with the sharp corners rounded off. Above the upper boundary, as usual, the energy spectrum becomes continuous—this is the state of molecules that have dissociated into atoms. In the well there are up to a hundred levels, the lower ones being equidistant from each other so that Figure 24 is a good approximation to the true situation for a large number of the lower levels.

The discrete nature of the energy levels and, in general, the discrete nature of the states, have a direct analogy in other cases of wave motion. Thus an infinitely deep square-well potential corresponds exactly to a string with rigidly fixed ends. An integral number of half wavelengths must fit into the length of the string. The fundamental tone corresponds to one half wave, the first overtone corresponds to two, and so on. A well of finite depth may be compared to a string fixed not rigidly but elastically, for example, a string fixed to two long flexible rods. The energy spectra of particles in the well correspond to the frequency spectrum of the oscillations of the string.

De Broglie's idea was formulated in relation to the free motion of particles. Schrödinger proposed that in the case of bound motion phenomena arise that are analogous to the oscillations of strings, i.e., a discrete set of possible states. Waves of any wavelength are possible in an infinite string, which corresponds to a continuous spectrum. Even before Schrödinger, it was known that energy may be quantized and that approximate methods existed, proposed in 1913 by Bohr, for finding the energy levels, but only Schrödinger was able to deduce quantization naturally from the general principles of wave motion. At the same time, Schrödinger's wave equation in the limiting case of very small wavelengths leads to the classical laws of motion, just as ray optics can be obtained from wave optics in the limiting case. Thus Hamilton's optical-mechanical analogy (see Chapter One) is considerably extended; it operates not only when optics is reduced to rays and mechanics to trajectories, but in the wave region too. While in Hamilton's time (1825) this analogy may have been regarded as a mathematical curiosity, after Schrödinger's discovery in 1925 it acquired a deep physical significance.

The general properties of wave motion allow even more important deductions. For example, it is well known that the greater the number of "nodes" (nonoscillating points) on a string, the higher the frequency of the string. When the length of the string is exactly one-half wavelength, there are no such points. This is the fundamental frequency of the string. The first overtone corresponds to one node, and so on. In a similar manner, the more "nodes" or "zeros" the wave function has, the higher the energy level of the particle. This is easy to understand: the more nodes (or zeros) there are, the shorter the de Broglie waves; but the wavelength is inversely proportional to the velocity. The velocity, which is in inverse ratio to the wavelength, is in direct ratio to the number of zeros (or nodes) of the wave function. Thus, the energy increases with the number of nodes.

Let us now apply the wave analogy to a question that was treated at the beginning of this chapter. We said that in a thin layer of an optically rare substance light may be propagated at an angle greater than the angle of total internal reflection. We likened the incidence of a wave at such an angle to the incidence of a particle on the wall of a potential well of finite depth. It is now easy to see what will correspond to the thin layer—a fairly small "potential barrier" beyond which there is once again a region of lower potential energy. For a particle moving according to the classical laws, it does not matter in the least what lies beyond the barrier: the particle cannot penetrate the barrier. However, in the case of quantum motion, the picture is quite different.

For our discussion we shall not choose the idealized case of a rectangular barrier, but shall turn immediately to a real physical problem. We shall begin by reminding the reader what is meant by the alpha decay of a radioactive nucleus. In such decay, a helium nucleus is spontaneously ejected from a heavy nucleus. The helium nucleus consists of two protons and two neutrons and is called an alpha particle. The reader may ask: why a helium nucleus and not, say, a single proton or neutron? The reason is that nuclear forces, although very large, become saturated, like chemical valency forces. In an alpha particle, the nuclear forces are highly saturated, and the particle is comparatively weakly bound to the rest of the nucleus. In the case of an individual proton or neutron, the nuclear forces are not saturated and hence these particles are strongly bound to the remaining protons and neutrons in the nucleus. They cannot escape from it spontaneously, unless external energy is supplied to the nucleus.

Let us now try to describe the approximate form of the potential curve for an alpha particle in the nucleus. Both the nucleus and the alpha particle carry positive charges. Hence there is an electrostatic repulsive force between them, at least when they become separated by a distance at which the nuclear forces (which bind strongly but act only over short distances) no longer operate. The potential energy curve for a repulsive force has the same form as the curve in Figure 21 but, as we said at the time, lies above the r axis.

Until it escapes, the alpha particle is bound to the nucleus; i.e., it is in a potential well, the form of which we do not know precisely. However, since nuclear forces act over short distances, the walls of the well must be comparatively steep (in comparison with the long-range, repulsive Coulomb force). This form of the potential energy curve for the nuclear forces shows that the particle will cease to experience nuclear forces once it leaves the limits of the nucleus. More precisely, this is the definition of the "boundary of the nucleus."

The form of the potential curve as a whole is shown in Figure 26. The broken line indicates the approximate place where the electrical forces begin to prevail over the nuclear ones. The diagram also shows the magnitude of the total energy. At an infinite distance from the nucleus this must lie above the potential energy curve so that the alpha particle

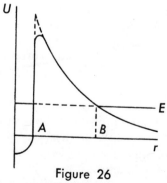

Figure 26

can have a positive kinetic energy. Otherwise it would always remain bound in the nucleus, like the particle in the potential well in Figures 22b and 23. The energy of an individual proton or neutron lies on a curve similar to Figure 26 but below the r axis. This indicates that it is impossible for it to escape from the nucleus. The fact that an alpha particle has an excess of energy sufficient for it to escape is explained, as we have said, by the saturation of the nuclear forces within it. That is why the well is shallower for alpha particles than for individual nucleons (protons or neutrons).

Between A and B (Fig. 26) the total energy is less than the potential. If the motion of the alpha particle obeyed the laws of classical mechanics, then for the given energy it could not cross the region AB nor escape from the nucleus at all. In quantum mechanics, however, the alpha particle *can* penetrate the barrier; i.e., it can enter the classically forbidden region and move out beyond the barrier.

The passage of the alpha particle through the barrier is analogous to incomplete reflection of light from a thin layer of optically rare material; but it must not be assumed that it can easily get past the barrier. If that were so, an alpha particle would never be found in the parent nucleus at all. In fact the wave function suffers such strong attenuation across the barrier that the probability of crossing it and escaping from the nucleus is extremely small. If we assume that a particle in the nucleus "runs" from one side to the other, then each time it "hits" the side it has one chance in 10^{39} of getting out. On the terrestrial time scale, this would correspond to a prison sentence of 10^{10} years, i.e., 10,000 million years for the alpha particle.

Unlike a prisoner serving a fixed term, each time the particle "hits" the side, the probability of escape, although very small, is always the same. A particle may remain in the nucleus a very short time or a very long time. It is completely impossible to predict in advance just when a given alpha particle will escape, just as it is impossible to predetermine at what point a given electron will strike the photographic plate in the diffraction experiment. The probabilistic nature of the law of alpha decay is a direct consequence of the uncertainty principle.

In addition to long-lived radioactive nuclei, there are some that decay on the average in 10^{-5} seconds. On the nuclear scale, this is also a very long time: there is one chance in 10^{17} of the particle escaping every time it hits the side. This differs from the previous case by a factor of 10^{22}. The energy of the short-lived nucleus, which it transmits to the alpha particle, is only twice as great as that of a long-lived one (two and 10^{22})! No classical laws could explain such a strong dependence of the time of decay on the energy. In quantum mechanics the penetrability of the barrier is calculated in a completely natural manner. The fundamental nature of the law is deduced even without taking the radius of the nucleus into account; the only terms required are the charge of the nucleus, the velocity of the escaping alpha particle and, of course, Planck's constant. If we carry out the formal process of going to the limit of classical mechanics by letting Planck's constant tend to zero, the probability of alpha decay becomes zero. Hence it would be hopeless to try to deduce the law of alpha decay somehow on the basis of classical ideas.

The quantum law of alpha decay was discovered in 1927 by Gamow, Condon and Gurney, independently of each other. This was one of the first triumphs of the young science of quantum mechanics, which was still at that time not universally recognized.

4 Motion of electrons in an atom

In popular accounts the atom is represented by a "cocoon"—i.e., a nucleus surrounded by the trajectories of electrons. At one time the structure of the atom was actually supposed to have this form. The nucleus was discovered in 1911 by Rutherford, and in order to explain why the electrons did not fall into it, it was naturally assumed that they moved in orbits like the planets around the sun. After all, Newton's law of gravitation and Coulomb's law of attraction seem very similar. In both cases the force is proportional to the square of the distance.

However, immediately the following difficulty arose: an electron moving in an orbit experiences a centrifugal acceleration. From the theory of electromagnetism it is known that an accelerating charge must emit electromagnetic waves that gradually drain away its energy. It follows that an electron moving in an orbit would finally have to fall into the nucleus.

This deduction is in striking conflict with experience: atoms are stable and electrons do not fall into the nucleus; hence the planetary model of the atom is inadequate.

Nevertheless, in 1913 Bohr found an extremely satisfactory solution for the problem: he supposed that in spite of the laws of electrodynamics there are orbits in which an electron emits no radiation, and he gave a simple rule for finding where these must be. Bohr was unable to justify this rule theoretically, but he guessed that these separate discrete orbits were somehow connected with the then still unknown quantum laws of motion. The peculiarity of quantum motion was revealed here by the fact that out of all the orbits that could be imagined, only certain ones were possible. In contrast, the orbits of the planets could be quite different and the laws of classical mechanics would not be contradicted. The peculiarity of quantum motion lies in the fact that only certain states of motion are possible in the atom.

Later, when quantum mechanics was created, it turned out that Bohr's hypothesis of stable orbits followed as an approximate rule. Originally Bohr himself used the classical laws of motion in conjunction with the alien postulate of the stability of certain select orbits.

Even in this imperfect form, the theory had a remarkable success. The spectrum of the hydrogen atom (i.e., the set of all the optical frequencies it radiates), followed quite naturally from it. Long before Bohr, Balmer had found an empirical formula for the frequencies in the hydrogen spectrum, and Bohr deduced this formula from his own postulates of motion. The first postulate stated that the angular momentum (see Chapter Two) of an electron in an orbit is an integral multiple of Planck's constant divided by 2π. The second postulate was that in a transition from one orbit to another light is radiated with a frequency equal to the energy difference between the orbits, divided by h.

Why are there such orbits? Only modern quantum mechanics can answer this question. Bohr himself could not do it, and hence he called his supposition a postulate. How did he guess that Planck's constant must be divided by 2π in order to obtain the angular momentum in the orbit? According to his own words, no other coefficients would fit Balmer's formula. What, then, of the second postulate? By 1913 it was known that light is emitted and absorbed as quanta of energy $h\nu$. Hence the second postulate simply expresses the law of conservation of energy on emission and absorption of electromagnetic waves. We shall have more to say on the origin of these light quanta and their relationship to the wave theory of light.

When attempts were made to apply Bohr's theory to atoms more complicated than hydrogen atoms agreement with experiment was by no means always satisfactory. Moreover, Bohr's theory was completely unable to explain why a hydrogen molecule consisting of two protons and two electrons (or even the positive ion of the hydrogen molecule, in which there are two protons and one electron) could be stable.

In the previous chapter it was shown that a bound particle cannot have just any energy; its energy is quantized. An electron bound in an atom obeys this rule perfectly. This follows without special postulates from the general laws of quantum mechanics.

However, in quantum mechanics motion does not take place in trajectories, and even the concept of a definite path becomes meaningless. This is clear from the uncertainty relationships, from which it follows that an electron in an atom has no trajectory. In fact the linear dimensions of the atom are of the order of 10^{-8} cm. This value must be taken for x in the uncertainty relationship. Then $\Delta p = h/\Delta x$ or 6.6×10^{-19}, and since the mass of an electron is 9×10^{-28} g, the uncertainty in the velocity is 0.75×10^9 cm/sec. The uncertainty in the kinetic energy can now be found from the formula

$$\Delta E = \tfrac{1}{2}m(\Delta v)^2 = 2.2 \times 10^{-10} \text{ ergs}$$

Since one electron-volt equals 1.6×10^{-12} ergs, the uncertainty in the energy is about 140 eV.

But the potential energy of the electron in the field of the nucleus is far less. This too is quite easy to estimate. The force on the electron due to the nucleus is e^2/r^2 by Coulomb's law, and the corresponding potential energy is $-e^2/r$. If we substitute Δx for r and 4.8×10^{-10} absolute electrostatic units for the charge e, we find that the potential energy is of the order of 2.5×10^{-11} ergs or about 14.5 eV. We have, however, already seen that the uncertainty in the kinetic energy is 140 eV. How are we to understand this? Clearly, we cannot divide the energy of motion of the electron in an atom into kinetic and potential energy. For if the kinetic energy were found to exceed the potential energy, the total energy in Figure 21 would lie above the r axis, which means that the kinetic energy of the electron is positive even at infinity. The electron will thus escape from the atom, which is in conflict with the supposed stable existence of the hydrogen atom. It follows that we are not allowed to divide total energy into kinetic and potential energies when we seek an estimate of the uncertainty in the position of the trajectory of the electron.

Hence the supposition that there is a definite electron trajectory in the atom leads to variables with uncertainties that are several times greater than the variables themselves. It follows that there can be no such trajectories.

In view of the great importance of this result we shall try to deduce it again somewhat differently. In order that the electron be bound to the nucleus, the kinetic energy must be less than the potential, i.e., less than 2.5×10^{-11} ergs. Hence it is easy to see that the velocity cannot exceed 2.3×10^8 cm/sec. The de Broglie wavelength is h/mv, so that it is bound to be greater than 10^{-7} cm; but this is ten times greater than the size of the atom itself, and so it is clear that if the motion takes place in a region that is ten times smaller than the corresponding wavelength it is impossible to speak of any trajectory. The atom is thus a typical quantum-mechanical object. The representation of the atom as a tangle of trajectories is simply a symbol, something quite conventional and arbitrary.

The actual properties of the motion of an atomic electron are described by quantum mechanics, and its energy corresponds to one of the possible levels in a potential well of the form shown in Figure 21. However, now there is nothing left that resembles a trajectory. If we attempt even to represent the atom on paper, we must surround the nucleus by a "smeared" cloud. The density of the cloud at a given point must correspond to the probability of finding the electron at that point, i.e., to the square of the amplitude of the wave function. It is not the electron itself that is smeared, but its wave function.

It follows from the uncertainty principle that an atomic electron of given energy has an undefinable position. What will happen if we still try to measure it? The linear dimensions of the atom are of the order of 10^{-8} cm, and in order for "position" to have some meaning, we must measure it to better than, say, 10^{-9} cm.

To obtain an accuracy of 10^{-9} in the measurement of position, we have to direct at our atomic electron another electron with a de Broglie wavelength of 10^{-9} cm. If they collide, then the atomic electron has actually been recorded in a sufficiently small region of space.

The "measuring" electron has a velocity of 0.7×10^{10} cm/sec—this is easily calculated from its de Broglie wavelength. The energy is also simple to calculate—14,000 eV. When an electron with so much energy strikes an atomic electron, it will transfer a large fraction of its energy to the latter. How much, precisely? It is impossible to answer this question, since the impact takes place somewhere in a region of 10^{-9} cm. It is equally impossible to say anything more precise about it since that was the de Broglie wavelength of the incident electron. Consequently we do not know exactly how the process of impact took place; did the electrons collide "head-on" or only "touch" each other lightly? As a result of the measurement, the electron that we have been examining has obtained an indeterminate momentum (indeterminate energy). This shows how the determination of position in quantum mechanics differs from the process of applying a ruler to a motionless body, which is what we understand by measurement in classical physics. Quantum measurement has a considerable effect on the measured object, and this effect increases with the increasing accuracy of the measurement. In classical mechanics it is always assumed that measurement has no influence at all on the system to which it is applied. Observing a planet does not, of course, produce any difference in its motion; but the same does not apply to the measurement of electrons.

The unknown momentum transmitted during the measurement of position is just that required by the uncertainty principle for the given accuracy of measuring the position. We have already shown that the uncertainty Δx in the position is of the order of λ. The oncoming particle may transmit any momentum from zero to its total momentum p, so that the uncertainty Δp in the momentum equals p. By de Broglie's relationship $p = h/\lambda$, and hence $\Delta p \Delta x = p\lambda = h$.

It is sometimes asked: if particles were discovered that were much lighter than electrons, would that not improve the accuracy of our measurements on electrons? We have just seen, however, that the mass of the particle did not come into our discussion at all. Provided that Planck's constant has a finite value, the process of measurement will disturb any system, and it will be impossible to control any disturbance. Of course, for macroscopic systems the disturbance is negligible, but for hypothetical particles lighter than electrons everything will be just the same as for electrons. The same uncertainty relationship $\Delta p \Delta x = h$ will apply to these particles, so that when they collide with electrons, the accuracy of measurement will not be improved. Moreover, it is already known that there are particles "lighter" than electrons; for example, photons have zero mass.

The analysis of imaginary experiments, including that of the two colliding electrons, led Heisenberg and Bohr to the formulation of the uncertainty principle. Clearly it is not some defect in the method of measurement that is under discussion, but the very nature of the measuring process as applied to the microcosm.

We have already remarked that Einstein tried to find an imaginary experiment that would circumvent the uncertainty principle. In one instance he proposed the use of gravitational forces. However, Bohr pointed out that the gravitational field due to the light waves also taking part in Einstein's imaginary experiment would have to be taken into account, and this brought back the uncertainty principle $\Delta p \Delta x \sim h$.

If we analyze the source of our conviction that classical objects always move along trajectories, we find that this is connected with the possibility that unrestricted measurement has no effect on the objects. For quantum objects this is impossible not because of any defects in experimental methods, but because, and only because, Planck's constant has a finite value. There is therefore every foundation for concluding that in a given state an electron's position and momentum cannot both be physically real at the same time. We may have one or the other, or of course both, but only with some uncertainty. It is pointless to ask if they cannot be measured together because they do not exist simultaneously or, conversely, if they do not exist together because they cannot be measured simultaneously. It is one and the same assertion.

The purely negative statement of the uncertainty principle is not in itself sufficient for formulating the system of equations of quantum mechanics. Here the correspondence principle is of considerable importance. According to this principle, the same quantities are conserved under similar conditions in both quantum and classical mechanics. For example, we have already noted that angular momentum is conserved in a central force field.

The significance of the correspondence principle may also be seen from the following example. Suppose that we have to measure the energy of a quantum-mechanical system. The measurement will be performed with an apparatus that obeys the laws of classical mechanics. If the law of conservation of energy holds good in the whole system, consisting of the object and the apparatus, the energy imparted to the apparatus must equal the energy given up by the object, i.e., the quantum-mechanical system. Clearly, if the conservation law did not apply, this deduction would not be valid. It has not been obtained by pure guesswork but on the basis of experimental facts that confirm the applicability of the law of conservation of energy on the atomic scale. The same applies to the other conservation laws, e.g., those of angular and linear momentum. One can formulate quantum equations of motion from the correspondence principle.

We must not simply take this to mean that in quantum mechanics the wave function somehow replaces the trajectory of classical mechanics. Where does this wave function come from? We have said that every measurement modifies the state of a quantum-mechanical system so that it is in general totally different from what it was before measurement. Thus, as soon as we try to determine the state of a system, the system is generally no longer in that state.

In order to understand what is meant by measurement, let us consider a rough but useful analogy. Suppose that we have to test a quantity of matches for "strikability." If we were to strike all the matches in the batch, the test would be useless for practical purposes. We must test 1,000 or 10,000 matches chosen at random. If for example, 99 percent are satisfactory, then it is highly probable that the other matches, which were not tested, will also ignite in ninety-nine cases out of a hundred. If the original batch is uniform, the test indicates the striking power of the matches with increasing precision as the number of matches tested is increased.

In the diffraction experiment an electron that has already struck the photographic plate is, of course, in a completely different state from the one it was in when passing through the crystal. Nevertheless, if a clear diffraction pattern is produced on the plate, we may be sure that all other electrons emitted under the same conditions will be distributed over the plate in the same way. From the diffraction pattern, we can determine the velocity of the electrons, i.e., their state before they passed through the crystal. However, one cannot say in advance which point on the plate each individual electron will strike. The greater the number of tests, the better our understanding of the probability of an individual event.

When we toss a coin, the probability of its coming down "heads" is always one half, however many times we have tossed it before. This experiment also allows us to determine the probability of an event but not to predict the event itself. In principle, a coin could be tossed by some ultra-accurate device that would record its position and control its motion. However, the point of the game would then be gone because each individual event would be predetermined. The difference with electrons is that a controlling device of this kind cannot physically exist; this follows from the uncertainty principle. Even a single attempt to observe the trajectory destroys any chance of controlling the system. Such are the objective physical properties of the measurement process in quantum mechanics: measurement yields the probability amplitude for a system before it is subjected to measurement. For this purpose we have to "spoil" a certain number of similar systems; but in principle we may always assume that there are many more systems of the same kind left that have not been "spoiled" by measurement. Hence in the whole set of systems, measured and unmeasured, measurement determines the state prevailing before it was performed, i.e., something depending not on the observer but on nature itself. The wave function for the system yields the probability that a given result will be obtained as a result of measurement before measurement is performed.

The electron motion in an atom has its own set of wave functions corresponding to the possible quantum states. In the present chapter we shall define these states with reference to a single electron. The properties of all the electrons in an atom taken together will be considered later.

The quantum state is characterized by the full set of conserved quantities, which may be found by using the correspondence principle. Firstly, energy must be conserved in the atom, if no external forces are doing work on it (such forces may be produced, for example, by the variable electromagnetic field of a light wave or a moving electron). If the atom is isolated from such disturbances, its energy will be conserved, just as the energy of a classical system that is isolated from external disturbances is conserved. We shall, assuming that the nucleus and all the other electrons give rise to a constant resultant field that acts on the given electron, for the time being apply the law of conservation of energy to the motion of an individual electron in the atom. This is quite sufficient for classifying the states of the electron.

We may take the field acting on the electron to be a central one; i.e., we assume that the total force acting on the electron always points strictly towards the nucleus. The angular momentum, conserved as explained in Chapter Two, can then be used as a basis for the further classification of atomic states. The classification is made easier because the component of the angular momentum along any axis drawn through the nucleus can only equal some integral multiple of $h/2\pi$. It is convenient to enumerate the states by integers, just as is done with any other objects.

We shall now prove this fundamental property of angular momentum in quantum mechanics. First of all we define the concept of a component of angular momentum along an axis. Figure 15 shows the plane of motion of a particle and the axis perpendicular to this place; the angular momentum is calculated with respect to this axis, and is said in this case to be parallel to it. Then using the ordinary rules we can find its component along any other axis. In this sense the angular momentum has the properties of a vector, i.e., a directed quantity.

By considering the uncertainty relationships for the angular momentum, we see that a radius of rotation exists simultaneously with the component of the momentum p perpendicular to it. The total length of the circumference $2\pi r$ must be an integral multiple of the de Broglie wavelength λ. If this were not so, the phase of the wave at a given point would not be single valued; every time we made an imaginary revolution round the axis, we would obtain a new phase at the given point. This is incompatible with the definition of phase.

It follows that the condition for the phase of the wave function to be single valued is $2\pi r = k\lambda$, where k is an integer. Multiplying both sides of the first equation by p and remembering that $\lambda = h/p$, we have $2\pi rp = kh$, and since $rp = M$, we conclude that the component of the angular momentum along a given axis can only take one of the values $hk/2\pi$.

In particular, k may equal zero. This means that the angular momentum is zero with respect to the given axis. Negative values of k correspond to rotation in the opposite direction.

We must not think that there is no rotation when $k = 0$; rest is impossible in quantum mechanics. By the uncertainty principle, if a particle is at rest and has a given azimuth ϕ, then it has no angular momentum, not even zero angular momentum. All values of ϕ are equally probable for any value of k, and when $k = 0$, motion in either direction—clockwise or counterclockwise—is equally probable.

In classical mechanics, the angular momentum of a particle about an axis is zero when it is moving in the same plane containing the axis; but in quantum mechanics it is impossible to represent motion so explicitly in the case $k = 0$. The particle is revolving about the axis in both directions at once. This would, of course, be impossible if particles moved along trajectories. We have already learned, however, that quantum particles obey nonclassical laws of motion. For example, when a particle strikes a crystal and is scattered, the scattering takes place on every plane simultaneously.

Stern and Gerlach verified the quantization of the angular momentum in an experiment that was as important for quantum mechanics as was the experimental demonstration of the diffraction of electrons. Before describing this experiment we must explain certain magnetic properties of the moving electron.

Unlike electrical charges, magnetic poles can never be separated, and therefore an elementary magnet can be represented by a small compass needle. In fact, however, magnetic action is always produced by currents, and in order to set up the same magnetic field as that of the needle (but at a distance considerably greater than the size of the magnet), it is sufficient to take a circular loop with an electric current flowing in it. In an external magnetic field such a loop, provided it can turn freely, will behave like a compass needle and may be used instead of a compass in the earth's field.

The relative positions of the needle and the loop are as follows: the needle is placed at the center of the loop and perpendicular to its plane. If when looking at the loop we see that the current is flowing counterclockwise, then the north pole of the magnet is facing us.

All this refers only to the positions of the loop and the needle. We have to compare their forces, i.e., the magnetic field they set up. For this, the needle and the loop must have equal magnetic moments. The magnetic moment of the current loop is equal to the product of the current strength and the area enclosed by the loop, divided by the velocity of light c. The proof of this is given in books on electromagnetism.

Let us now turn to the electron. A revolving electron is equivalent to a current. If it performs n revolutions per second and its charge is $-e$* then a total charge of $-ne$ per second will pass through any plane perpendicular to the motion. By definition, this is the current strength $i = -ne$. The area enclosed by the loop is πr^2, so that the magnetic moment set up by the electron is $\mu = -ne\pi r^2/c$. The electron travels a distance of $2\pi rn$ per second, so this is its velocity v. Accordingly, the magnetic moment may also be written in terms of the velocity in the form $\mu = -erv/2c$. Let us now divide the numerator and the denominator by the mass of the electron m and replace the product mv by p, the momentum of the electron. The product rp is the angular momentum M, so that the magnetic moment of the electron due to its orbital motion is propor-

* The minus sign here and in the following discussion is connected with the fact that the electron has a negative charge.

tional to its angular momentum. We often say too that the magnetic moment is proportional to the angular momentum $\mu = -eM/2mc$.

We have just seen that the component of the angular momentum along a given axis is quantized, so that the component of the magnetic moment is also quantized and takes one of the values $\mu = -(eh/4\pi mc)k$. The coefficient of the integer k is the natural unit of magnetic moment for the electron. The unit of magnetic moment is called the Bohr magneton and is equal to 10^{-20} in the CGS system of units.

A particle with a magnetic moment tends to be attracted to the poles of a magnet. Probably everyone has seen iron filings collect around the ends of a magnet. They become magnetized by the field and themselves become magnetic. In an external field they turn into alignment with the field just like a compass needle, but then the north pole of the little magnet is somewhat closer to the south pole of the big magnet (which is causing the field), so that the resultant field attracts the little magnet toward the big one. Since in a uniform magnetic field both poles of the little magnet experience equal and opposite forces, the little magnet simply turns but does not change its position. The attractive power of a magnet is caused by the lines of force being crowded together at the poles.

Let us return to the Stern-Gerlach experiment illustrated in Figure 27. One pole of a magnet, say the north pole, is shaped like a wedge, so that the lines of force are crowded together at the point. A beam of atoms is directed parallel to the edge of the wedge. These atoms come from a small crucible in which a suitable substance is heated until it vaporizes and is directed into the beam. The energy required for vaporization does not usually change the energy state of the atoms, so that they emerge in their ground state, i.e., with the least possible internal energy. We have already said that since an atomic electron experiences a central force the angular momentum as well as the energy is conserved.

Consider an axis drawn vertically upward, and suppose that

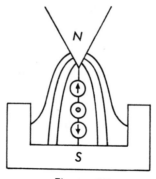

Figure 27

the number k, which gives the component of the angular momentum along this axis, can assume the three values $k = +1$, 0, -1. If there is a component $+1$, then there must also be a component -1, since the "up" and "down" directions are chosen in a purely conventional manner. There are atoms in the beam with all these values of k. The atoms for which $k = +1$ have magnetic moments in the opposite direction to the magnetic field. Their south poles point toward the north pole of the external magnet. This means that they must be attracted toward the point of the wedge. Atoms for which $k = -1$ are repelled from the point, and atoms for which $k = 0$ experience no force at all. As a result, those atoms for which $k = 1$ are deflected upward, those for which $k = -1$ are deflected downward, and those with $k = 0$ continued undeflected. The original beam is thus split into three separate beams. If the angular momentum were not quantized and could take any desired value, as in classical mechanics, then instead of three separate beams we would obtain a continuous fan. The Stern-Gerlach experiment thus provides direct evidence of the quantization of angular momentum.

Let us now consider further properties of the angular momentum. We have already said that it is a vector quantity, i.e., it may be resolved in three mutually perpendicular directions. Such a resolution is shown in Figure 28. In the xyz system the

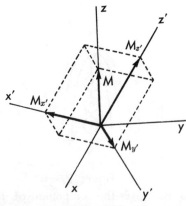

Figure 28

angular momentum lies along the z axis and its components in the x and y directions are zero, but in the $x'y'z'$ system, which has been rotated with respect to the first one, the angular momentum has components $M_{x'}$, $M_{y'}$, $M_{z'}$. If we construct a parallelepiped with sides $M_{x'}$, $M_{y'}$, $M_{z'}$, then M will be the diagonal. By Pythagoras' theorem it is given by $M^2 = M_{x'}^2 + M_{y'}^2 + M_{z'}^2$. Let us consider what this means in quantum mechanics.

For this purpose, we shall return to the Stern-Gerlach experiment. What will happen if we turn the magnet with respect to the beam through a small angle, say $10°$? This makes no difference to the beam of atoms, there is neither "up" nor "down" nor any other special direction for them. The original beam will again be split in the magnetic field into the three beams as before, so that, let us say, both M_z and $M_{z'}$ will take identical integral values, with the z and z' axes inclined at $10°$ to each other. At first glance this seems impossible. If we measure off a conventional unit of length in one direction and then take its projection on a straight line inclined at $10°$ to the original direction, then the projection (component) will equal 0.986, which is clearly not an integer. Within the framework of classical mechanics this paradox cannot be resolved.

The fact is that the two components of the angular momentum on different axes cannot exist simultaneously. We cannot have, say, one component $M_{z'} = 0.986h/2\pi$ and another $M_{x'} = 0.16h/2\pi$. This is in agreement with Pythagoras' theorem: $0.986^2 + 0.16^2 = 1$, but it does not agree with quantum mechanics. There is one angular momentum and only one z component. In the case we have been discussing this has only three possible values, $+1$, 0, and -1. $M_{x'}$ and $M_{y'}$ are simply not equal to anything at all; they do not exist. When one component of the angular momentum is known, it is impossible to determine the two other components exactly, just as it is impossible to determine position and momentum simultaneously in the same state. A definite physical state of the system can possess one and only one z component of the angular momentum, which is thus quite different from the other vector quantity—the linear momentum, the three components of which may simultaneously have precise values.

Now let one of the beams into which the original beam was split be passed through another such magnet. If the second magnet is parallel in space to the first, the beam will not be split again, since it has already been sorted out by the first magnet, and the M_z components of all the atoms are the same. Hence all its atoms are deflected the same amount in the second magnet, and if the beam with $k = 0$ is chosen, there is no deflection at all.

It is sufficient to turn the second magnet through some angle to split any of the three beams once again into three. For the angular momentum has no definite component in the new direction of the magnetic field. The angular momentum does not have components simultaneously in the two directions, old and new. The state with $M = hk/2\pi$ does not correspond to any definite k', i.e., $M_{z'}$. It is made up of three states with $k' = 1$, 0, or -1, if $M_{z'} = hk'/2\pi$. On the other hand, the state with $k' = 1$, i.e., with definite $M_{z'}$, is resolvable into three others with $k = 1$, 0, and -1.

Any field will split the given initial beam into not more than three parts, no matter how many times it is passed through the magnetic field. We can never obtain five, seven, etc., beams. Only three values of the component of the angular momentum are obtained along a given axis: $h/2\pi$, 0, and $-h/2\pi$. Let us measure the angular momentum in units of $h/2\pi$. Clearly this is the most natural unit. We can then say that the maximum component of the beam under consideration will never exceed 1 (in other cases it can be 2, 3, or higher). In classical mechanics we would be able to make a simple deduction from this: if the component of the angular momentum vector can never exceed a certain value, then the angular momentum itself, i.e., its absolute magnitude, must equal that value. The maximum component of a vector is equal to the absolute magnitude of the vector itself. Does it not follow from this that the absolute magnitude of the angular momentum in the beam, which for any splitting gives a maximum component equal to 1, is itself 1?

We must not hurry our argument. The absolute value of the angular momentum is, as always, $M^2 = M_x + M_y^2 + M_z^2$. But when $M_z = 1$ we cannot assert that $M_y = M_x = 0$. In general, the three components of the angular momentum do not simultaneously exist, so that when $M_z = 1$, M_x and M_y do not equal anything at all.

The value of M^2 may be deduced as follows. Let us suppose that the beam lies along the x axis, and that the magnetic field is directed first along the y axis and then along the z axis. What will be the *mean* value of M_z^2? We shall always obtain three beams, no matter how the magnetic field is oriented. In two beams of the three $M_z^2 = 1$ and in the other $M_z^2 = 0$. In any case, the mean value of M_z^2 equals $\frac{2}{3}$. Similarly, the mean value of M_y^2 will again equal $\frac{2}{3}$, since it makes no difference which axis we call the z axis and which we call the y axis. Now let us suppose that the beam is traveling along the y axis. The mean value of M_x^2 is once more $\frac{2}{3}$. Since the mean value of M^2 must be equal to the sum of all three mean squares of the components, and each of the latter equals $\frac{2}{3}$, the mean value of M^2 equals $3 \times \frac{2}{3} = 2$. This result is only *determined* by the maximum component of the angular momentum; it is not equal to it. The mean value in all cases is the same, just like the maximum component itself. However, if averaging a quantity always gives the same value, it is useless to talk about the mean: we can simply say that this is the value itself. Thus the absolute magnitude of the angular momentum can exist simultaneously with one of its components, and the other two components do not exist. The angular momentum can have a component, but only along one axis at a time. This is usually, but not necessarily called the z component.

We should not be surprised that the absolute magnitude of the angular momentum is greater than its maximum z component. The mean squares of those components which do not have a strict meaning simultaneously with M_z make a definite contribution to the mean, and since squares are always positive, we have $M^2 = M_x^2 + M_y^2 + M_z^2 > M_z^2$.

True, there is one important exception: when the absolute magnitude of the angular momentum is zero, all three components are simultaneously equal to zero. Physically this is shown in the Stern-Gerlach experiment by the fact that the beam is simply not split at all, as if the field had no direction, which means that all components of the angular momentum are zero.

If the absolute magnitude of the angular momentum is not equal to zero, then the beam may be divided an infinite number of times by its successive passage through differently inclined fields. The z component of the angular momentum is therefore established anew each time. Each beam with a definite z component of the angular momentum in the direction of the previous field, acquires new components in the direction of the new field it is crossing and retains from the old field only the relative amplitudes for all three new components. If, for example, the new field is inclined at a small angle to the old, then the strongest beam will be the one in which the z component of the angular momentum is equal to the value in the old beam. Let the old component be equal to 1. After crossing a field that is inclined at a small angle to the preceding one, the beam for which the z component in the new field equals 1 will be the most intense. Beams with the other two components will also be present, although weaker.

In principle the splitting affects every individual atom, but the law is revealed only in experiments involving large numbers of individual atoms. This shows again the probabilistic nature of the quantum-mechanical laws.

Now that we have described the basic properties of angular momentum, we may consider the motion of an individual electron in an atom: we know all the constants that describe its motion in space. Later we shall find one more constant; however, this refers not to the motion of the electron in space but to its internal motion (see next chapter). We shall in the meantime classify the motion of the electron according to the constants of its motion in space or, as we say, its orbital motion. There are three such constants: the energy, the absolute magnitude of angular momentum, and the angular momentum's z component, which is always an integral multiple of $h/2\pi$.

In this connection it is very important to return once more to the following problem. To what extent does an individual electron in an atom really possess all these values independently of the other electrons? Of course, only a hydrogen atom possesses a single electron; all other atoms have as many electrons as are needed to neutralize the charge on the nucleus (the number is equal to the atomic number of the element in Mendeleyev's periodic table). In fact, there is a very complicated force acting on each electron. The many-body problem has not been solved analytically even in classical mechanics. Indeed, it is even more complicated in quantum mechanics, and cannot be solved numerically even on high-speed computers, although it is possible that modifications of currently available computers will make such solutions possible in the future.

However, in quantum mechanics we may successfully apply an approximate semiquantitative method that will take us a very long way in understanding all the fundamental laws of motion of electrons in complicated atoms. This method was proposed by Hartree and much improved by Fok. In this method the actions of all the other electrons on the one under consideration are replaced by a mean force. According to Fok, this is not simply the field of the smeared charge of the electron cloud (as the probability field is called). Since it is impossible to track the motion of an individual electron and the electrons are indistinguishable from each other, the quantum-mechanical phenomenon of "exchange" occurs when there is some interaction. This depends not only on the probability of finding the electron at this or that point, but also on the phase of the wave function. When we calculate the exchange interaction between electrons, we take each of them to be simultaneously in two states. In principle the electrons can only be in these states one at a time, but the interaction "mixes them up," so that it is impossible to say which of the electrons is in a given state. According to Fok the agreement between the theory and experiment is substantially improved when exchange is taken into account.

The field due to all the other electrons on the electron under consideration is called the "self-consistent" field. It allows us to replace the many-body problem approximately by an equivalent one-body problem. We note that "exchange" occurs in the equations as a result of the application of an approximate method; it does not occur in the exact equations.

It is very important that the self-consistent Hartree-Fok field is central, because the electron then possesses the same constants of motion as in the hydrogen atom, where the field is simply a Coulomb field. This permits the states of an electron in any atom to be classified just as in the hydrogen atom: by energy, angular momentum, and z component of angular momentum along an arbitrary direction.

Strictly speaking, an individual electron in an atom does not have a total angular momentum or total energy; these parameters refer to the atom as a whole. However, a qualitative description based on the concept of separate states of each electron in the field of all the others always gives satisfactory results. It allows the true state of the whole atom (for which we still cannot calculate the wave function) to be compared in a one-to-one correspondence with some approximate state that can be characterized by constants of motion of the individual electrons.

Little can be added to what was said in the previous chapter concerning the energies of individual electrons. Although energy calculations are fairly complicated, computers may be used to solve them approximately. Bound states correspond to a discrete spectrum, and free states to a continuous one. The free state of an electron in an atom corresponds not to the atom but to a positive ion near which the electron is moving. Such an electron may either move "past" or else emit a quantum of light (a photon) and become bound to the atom (this is called free-bound emission). In the latter case the photon must remove sufficient energy from the electron, so that it no longer has a continuous but a discrete spectrum. Sometimes the photon takes away less energy than is necessary for this to occur. The electron then remains free even after emission. This is called free-free emission; it is important when matter is heated so strongly that all the atoms are completely ionized—i.e., when they lose all their electrons.

Calculating the energy of an electron is difficult because the energy depends on the actual form of the field acting on the electrons. On the other hand, angular momentum does *not* depend on the form of the field at all; it is only necessary for the field to be central. Then and only then is the angular momentum conserved (i.e., it characterizes the state).

As we have shown, the magnitude of the angular momentum is determined by its maximum z component. For a specific electron this integer is denoted by ℓ, the *azimuthal quantum number*. The term "quantum number" refers to any number that in some way describes a quantum state. The term "azimuthal" was adopted from the old theory of Bohr. In quantum mechanics the number ℓ denotes the state of motion of a particle not according to the azimuth, but rather according to the angle that is analogous to the geographical latitude of the point. The azimuth corresponds to the longitude ϕ (see Fig. 15), which is connected with the component of the angular momentum k, called the *magnetic* quantum number. We can understand this name if we recall that k can be determined with the aid of the Stern-Gerlach experiment according to the component of the magnetic moment in the direction of the external magnetic field.

The states $\ell = 0$, 1, 2, and 3 are called the *s, p, d,* and *f* states respectively. These terms were originally used in spectroscopy to denote certain spectral lines as "sharp," "principal," "diffuse," and "fundamental."

We found in the previous chapter that the greater the energy of the bound state, the greater the number of nodes or zeros of the wave function. This is also true for wave functions relating to other physical quantities that assume discrete values, e.g., the angular momentum. The argument of these functions is no longer the distance from the nucleus, but an angle analogous to the geographical latitude (more precisely, its complement to 90°). The nodal lines may be simply represented on the surface of a unit sphere. We have chosen the case when $k = 0$ (Fig. 29a). If $k \neq 0$, some nodal lines degenerate to

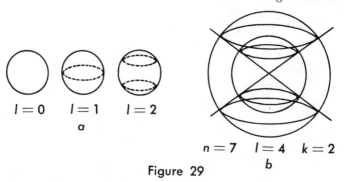

$l = 0$ $l = 1$ $l = 2$

a

$n = 7$ $l = 4$ $k = 2$

b

Figure 29

single points at the poles. The dependence of the wave function on the azimuth is complicated and itself has no zeros, but its real and imaginary parts vanish as many times as k is a multiple of unity.

5 Electron spin

In mechanics we often use the concept of a mass point, whose position in space is completely defined by three coordinates. A mass point in classical mechanics is by no means a point in the mathematical sense of the word. Thus the earth moves about the sun as if the masses of the earth and of the sun were entirely concentrated at these mass points. Their actual sizes have no significance at all. In fact the earth performs another motion as well—it rotates about its axis—but this internal motion does not affect the motion of its center of gravity. The difference between point and extended bodies in mechanics is determined by whether or not internal motion (if any) affects the motion of the center of gravity. In this sense a bullet is not a point since its rotation about its axis has a considerable effect on its flight through the air (otherwise why make it rotate?), but the earth does behave like a mass point.

When speaking about an electron in an atom we have so far considered the electron as a point. However, experiment shows that in fact the electron also possesses an internal motion, which is reminiscent of rotation about an axis. It certainly does not follow from this that the electron has geometric dimensions, for the laws of its rotation are simply not connected with any quantities similar to the radius of a rotating body. The internal motion in the case of an electron is a pure quantum-mechanical motion and cannot be considered the displacement of something in space. Unlike the rotation of the earth, the internal motion of an electron has a considerable effect on its state in the atom, and in this sense the earth is more like a point than an electron is!

Any physical concept is best defined by describing the phenomenon or experiment that reveals it and it alone. Let us suppose that the Stern-Gerlach experiment is carried out with hydrogen atoms in the state of least energy, i.e., the ground state. In these atoms the azimuthal quantum number is zero ($\ell = 0$), and hence the magnetic quantum number $k = 0$. Proceeding from this, one would expect that the beam of hydrogen atoms would not be split: the zero angular momentum would always have a zero z component. If the hydrogen atoms for some reason have an angular momentum, division into at least three beams would take place: for $\ell = 1$, k takes the values $+1$, 0, and -1. However, the beam does in fact split into *two*. Any integral angular momentum should give an odd number of z components (between 1 and -1, 2 and -2, etc.); but here the largest z component of the angular momentum must be equal to $\frac{1}{2}$. Then there is the other z component equal to $-\frac{1}{2}$; i.e., there are just two values of this component.

Our deduction that the angular momentum must have integral z components is based on the requirement that the phase of the wave function in space must be single valued. In other words it is caused entirely by the orbital motion. From the most general theorems of quantum mechanics it can be shown that the z component of angular momentum along any given axis may be in some cases an integral multiple and in other cases a half-integral multiple of $h/2\pi$; but according to the same theorem for a given angular momentum, the z component onto the axis will certainly change in steps of one. The reader must take this result on faith, since there is no easy way of proving this. If the largest z component is $\frac{1}{2}$, then there is only one other z component possible, namely $-\frac{1}{2}$. This is clearly just the example we considered in the Stern-Gerlach experiment for hydrogen atoms.

The half-integral value of the angular momentum indicates

that it is not connected with orbital motion. Consequently, the electron by definition must have some form of internal motion. The splitting of the beam in the magnetic field showed that under certain conditions this motion affects the orbital motion. An electron is thus not a material point in the mathematical sense; i.e., it also possesses some free internal motion. However, geometric concepts such as length do not apply at all to this matter. Angular momentum has the dimensions of Planck's constant, not of length.

If we must compare the internal motion with some classical concept, we may think of rigid-body rotation, e.g., a bullet in flight or a spinning top. The intrinsic angular momentum of an electron is called, for brevity as well as for historical reasons, the "spin." We have already said that in a central force field the angular momentum is conserved. Strictly speaking, this refers only to the *total* angular momentum, which is made up of the orbital and the spin angular momenta.

The splitting of the beam by the magnetic field is caused by the magnetic moment of the electron. Experiment shows that the proton in the hydrogen atom has the same spin angular momentum, with components $\pm\frac{1}{2}$, as the electron, but its magnetic moment is much smaller. Hence under ordinary experimental conditions the beam splitting is due solely to the electron magnetic moment, although in principle there should also be an additional "hyperfine" splitting due to the proton moment. We have already shown that the coefficient of proportionality between the magnetic moment and the orbital angular momentum of a charged particle is $e/2mc$. It is found, however, that in the case of the electron spin, the coefficient is e/mc, which is twice as great as that for orbital angular momentum. Since the spin z component in ordinary units is $h/4\pi$, the magnetic moment is $eh/4\pi mc$, i.e., one Bohr magneton. We shall see later that this result is in fact only approximate.

Our deduction of the relationship between the magnetic moment and angular momentum referred only to orbital motion. The new coefficient e/mc does not invalidate the deductions concerning the orbital motion. Dirac explained the coefficient with the aid of his own special wave equation for the electron. This equation differs from the ordinary Schrödinger equation because it takes into account the requirements of the theory of relativity and the internal spin motion of the electron. The coefficient e/mc is obtained automatically in Dirac's theory.

In the case of the proton the situation is quite different. The ratio of its magnetic moment to the angular momentum is 2.8 times greater than predicted by Dirac's theory. A neutron has no overall electric charge. Dirac's theory must therefore give it zero magnetic moment, but in fact the neutron does have a magnetic moment equal to -1.9 (in the same units as the magnetic moment of the proton). The minus sign indicates that the magnetic moment of the neutron is opposite to its spin.

We are still unable to explain these facts from any first principles. If we compare electrons and nuclear particles, we arrive at the following conclusions. The electron interacts with the electromagnetic field fairly weakly, and solely on account of its charge. The force of this interaction is so small that the electron may be considered an independent particle in an external electromagnetic field. Is there anything to prevent our using the same approach for the proton and the neutron? We have already seen that the specifically nuclear forces are considerably stronger than electromagnetic forces. The zero-order approximation, in which these forces are not taken into account, is so rough that it disagrees considerably with experimental data on the magnetic moments of nuclear particles. A better approximation cannot be formulated at present because no reliable method for calculating such strong forces as yet exists.

The difficulties with the magnetic moments of the proton and neutron do not indicate any disagreement of quantum mechanics with experiment. They must be referred to the theory of elementary particles, which is still incomplete. The quantum mechanics of Heisenberg and Schrödinger is not concerned with the structure of elementary particles. In their theory every particle is characterized by its mass, energy, and spin. The magnetic moment associated with the spin is assumed to be an additional property that must simply be taken into account as an experimental fact. Quantum mechanics for particles not subjected to nuclear forces is as complete and as consistent as the classical mechanics of Newton, and is to the same degree uninterested in the nature of moving particles.

This division of atomic physics into quantum mechanics and the theory of elementary particles is not at all artificial. When studying the structure of elementary particles, we are dealing with dimensions of the order of 10^{-13} cm and less. The corresponding uncertainty in the velocity turns out to be equal to, or greater than, the velocity of light (the latter is true for electrons); but at such high velocities the theory of relativity must be taken into account. Any physical theory that does so is said to be *relativistic*. Thus Dirac's theory is the relativistic quantum mechanics for electrons. This gives the correct gyromagnetic ratio for electrons. No relativistic theory of nuclear particles has yet been formulated. The forces acting at distances of the order of 10^{-13} cm are the very strong nuclear forces, whose nature has not yet been elucidated, whereas the forces acting on the electron are electromagnetic forces, about which enough is known. The general situation is that theory cannot yet predict the magnitude of the gyromagnetic ratio for the proton and the neutron as well as for many other nuclear phenomena.

Nonrelativistic quantum mechanics is concerned only with types of motion in which the velocities of the particles remain small in comparison with the velocity of light. The error introduced if relativistic effects are ignored is of the order of the ratio of the velocity of the particles to the velocity of light. Let us estimate this error for electrons in different atoms, i.e., atoms with atomic number Z running from 1 in hydrogen to

92 in uranium. Schrödinger's equation involves only the mass of the electron, its charge, and Planck's constant. In a strictly nonrelativistic theory the velocity of light plays no part. From m, e, and h it is possible to construct one and only one parameter with the dimensions of velocity. Let us do this. We have already seen that the potential energy of the Coulomb forces is equal to the squares of the charge divided by the distance. This means that (charge)^2 = (energy) × (length). Further, a quantum of energy is equal to the product of Planck's constant and the frequency. But frequency has the dimensions of the reciprocal of time, so that h = (energy) × (time). Let us now divide the first equation by the second. The dimensions of energy cancel and we are left with

$$\frac{(\text{charge})^2}{h} = \frac{\text{length}}{\text{time}} = \text{velocity}.$$

No other quantity with the same dimensions can be formulated from m, e, and h. We thus begin to suspect that the relativistic correction to Schrödinger's equation must be of the order of magnitude of the square of the charge divided by h and by the velocity of light. This is equal to the ratio of the velocity of an electron in an atom to the velocity of light. Calculations show that in fact this correction is larger by a factor of 2π (we have seen several times that h does not enter equations by itself but is often divided by 2π). Substituting numerical values for the constants we find $2\pi e^2/hc = 1/137$. This result is dimensionless and is therefore independent of our choice of system of units.

The transition to nonrelativistic theory formally consists in taking the velocity of light to be infinite, just as in passing to the classical theory from the quantum one h is taken to be zero. Of course, the error introduced by the nonrelativistic approximation is that a quantity that actually equals $1/137$ is taken to be infinitely small. (The nonrelativistic theory is correct for the hydrogen atom to the order $(1/137)^2$.) In an atom with atomic number Z, the error is of the order of

$(Z/137)^2$, which for uranium turns out to be about 0.45. However, when the estimated error is comparable with unity, the error in the variable under consideration is comparable with the variable itself, and calculations become imprecise. Schrödinger's nonrelativistic wave equation is then hardly applicable and complete agreement of theory and experiment is obtained only with Dirac's relativistic equation. Schrödinger's equation is satisfactory for all electrons in atoms with Z, say, up to ten. The relationship between the nonrelativistic and relativistic theories may be illustrated by the following scheme:

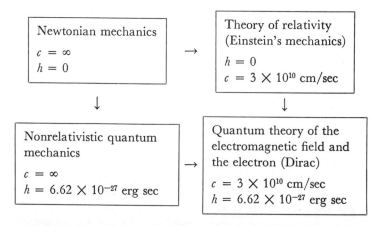

Only the second box on the right is incomplete because we have as yet no theory in which the ratio 1/137 could be obtained automatically. Moreover, nuclear forces are still not completely understood, and it is not clear whether the universal constants used up until now will be sufficient. The history of physics shows that whenever a new universal constant appears, there has to be a profound rethinking of the basic principles of physics.

Let us now return to the gyromagnetic ratio e/mc. This contains the velocity of light in its denominator, and according to the above classification is a relativistic quantity. Before we discuss what effect the magnetic moment has on the motion of an atomic electron, we must recall how it was discovered. The ratio $e/2mc$ was first introduced in the classical theory of the electron. Einstein then proposed verifying by an experiment the fact that this is the ratio of the magnetic moment to the angular momentum. He suggested that if magnetization of a steel rod produced a resultant magnetic moment of the electrons, then a resultant angular momentum should also appear. This experiment was carried out by de Haas and it was found that the ratio of the magnetic moment and the angular momentum was twice as great as the value given by classical electron theory, in which only the orbital motion of the electron was taken into account. The spin had still not been discovered and de Haas's result could not be understood. Later Uhlenbeck and Goudsmit discovered spin by analyzing spectroscopic data. It then became apparent that the magnetism of iron is connected with the spin of its electrons and not with their orbital motion.

Let us now consider the effect of spin on the orbital motion of electrons. We must first note that spin is extremely important for a proper understanding of the structure of many-electron atoms, i.e., in the many body problem of quantum mechanics. We shall consider this in the following chapter.

For the present we shall confine our attention to the "spin-orbit" interaction of a single electron. (In the Stern-Gerlach experiment this interaction was produced as a result of the application of the external magnetic field.) The cause of this interaction is now easy to understand: both the orbital motion and the spin have associated magnetic moments, and two magnets always interact with each other. The energy of this interaction is proportional to the product of the magnetic moments. Each of them contains the velocity of light in its denominator, so that an essentially relativistic expression is obtained that is inversely proportional to the square of the velocity of light. For an individual electron, the spin-orbit interaction may be quite rigorously calculated from Dirac's equation, and not merely as a correction. The picture of the two magnets is purely a means of visualizing the problem and cannot be used to give precise results.

Having estimated the order of magnitude of the effect of spin on orbital motion, we shall now discuss how it becomes apparent. The spin component has only two values in any given direction, e.g., in the direction of the orbital angular momentum. Hence if the maximum component of the orbital motion is as usual equal to ℓ, the total angular momentum (orbital plus spin) of the electron will have the maximum z components $\ell + \frac{1}{2}$ and $\ell - \frac{1}{2}$, depending on whether the spin is parallel or antiparallel to the orbital angular momentum. The difference between the energies of an electron with spin parallel and antiparallel to the orbital angular momentum is of the same order of magnitude as the energy of interaction of the two "magnets." As a result, the energy level of an atom with given ℓ splits into two sublevels or, as is said in spectroscopy, has a *fine structure*. The well-known yellow line of sodium is double because the excited level (from which the electron returns to the ground state with the emission of yellow light) exhibits fine-structure splitting into two sublevels.

How much smaller is the magnitude of the splitting than the distance between the original levels? We have already said that it contains c^2 in the denominator. This means that the corresponding relativistic correction for an atom with atomic number Z is $(2\pi Ze/hc)^2 = (Z/137)^2$. In very heavy atoms this may reach 0.45 so that the structure is no longer very "fine." In such cases it is better to use the exact solution of Dirac's equation rather than the approximate correction.

Many-electron atoms also have the spin-spin magnetic interaction. This must be distinguished from the spin-spin interaction of another kind that is important in many-body problems (see next chapter). The magnetic interaction of the spins also leads to a form of fine structure like that of the spin-orbit interaction. Since the atomic number of the element does not occur in the expression for the spin-spin magnetic energy, the latter leads to corrections that are comparable with the spin-orbit ones only for small values of Z. For large Z the spin-orbit interaction predominates over the spin-spin interaction.

The resultant angular momentum of the electron is denoted by j. Clearly

$$j = \ell + \tfrac{1}{2} \quad \text{or} \quad j = \ell - \tfrac{1}{2}$$

The nucleus also has a magnetic moment if it has angular momentum. For example, the deuteron, which consists of a proton and a neutron, has a resultant spin equal to 1. Hence the angular momenta of the proton and the neutron are parallel. These particles are in the s state in the deuteron, i.e., they have zero orbital angular momentum. Consequently the motion of the proton does not create an orbital magnetic moment. The entire magnetic moment of the deuteron must be of spin origin. We have already said that the magnetic moment of the proton equals 2.8, and that of the neutron -1.9 nuclear magnetons (this is 1836 times smaller than the value for electrons, since the mass appears in the denominator). Because the spins of the proton and the neutron are parallel, we must expect a deuteron magnetic moment equal to $2.8 - 1.9 = 0.9$. This is verified closely by experiment.

Using similar although more complicated arguments we can predict the magnetic moments of many light nuclei, and obtain close agreement with experiment.

The electron and nuclear magnetic moments also interact with each other like magnets, but since the nuclear moments are approximately a thousand times smaller the resultant splitting of the atomic levels is correspondingly smaller than the fine structure. This splitting is called the *hyperfine structure*.

How are we to calculate the number of hyperfine-structure sublevels into which a fine-structure level is divided? Let the total angular momentum of the electron be j and that of the nucleus J, and let us take the component of J along j. In this way, we obtain the following values of the resultant angular momentum F: $F = j + J, j + J - 1, \ldots, j - J$. For example, if $j = 3/2$ and $J = 1$, then $F = 5/2, 3/2, 1/2$. When the nuclear angular momentum is the larger, the resultant moment varies in a similar way from $J + j$ to $J - j$. This rule of addition of angular momenta applies in general to any two such momenta.

6 Structure of the atom

In the two preceding chapters we saw that the motion of an electron is characterized by its energy, angular momentum, z components of orbital angular momentum, and the spin z component along some axis. In a complicated atom these four quantities are not exact constants of motion for an individual electron. Nevertheless, the self-consistent field method allows (even if not rigorously) the separation of the motion of individual electrons because in quantum mechanics the state of a system is uniquely connected with the number of zeros in the wave function. This number is clearly always an integer. If it is found correctly for the approximate wave function, then this function will be a good representation of the exact function, even when the zeros or nodes of the approximate function do not occur at the same places as in the exact function. Similarly, a caricature may catch a likeness even if the correspondence between the individual parts is distorted.

At the end of Chapter Four we discussed the distribution of zeros in the angular momentum wave function and their dependence on the azimuth and latitude angles. The electron wave function also depends on the distance from the nucleus. Here the wave function may also have several zeros. If we return to the three-dimensional picture, these radial zeros lie on concentric spheres. The angular zeros lie on planes, which pass through the axis and cut the spheres along meridians, and on cones, which have a common vertex at the nucleus, and for which the parallels on the sphere represent the lines of intersection with the spheres. In Figure 29b there are two radial, two latitudinal, and two azimuthal surfaces on which the wave function becomes zero. The number of radial zeros is called the radial quantum number and is denoted by n_r. The maximum component of the angular momentum ℓ is called the azimuthal quantum number. In Figure 29b there are two azimuthal zeros (in the real and imaginary parts they are displaced with respect to each other and hence are not shown in the diagram), so that the magnetic quantum number is $k = 2$. Furthermore, there are two more zeros on the parallels, and hence the total number of angular zeros is $2 + 2 = 4$, so that $\ell = 4$. It is generally agreed that wave functions should be classified not by n_r but by the sum $n = n_r + \ell + 1$, which is called the principal quantum number of the electron. The convenience of using the principal quantum number may be seen from the fact that it is always greater than the azimuthal number. In our example, the principal quantum number is $n = 2 + 4 + 1 = 7$. For this value of n, the azimuthal quantum number can take the values 6, 5, 4, 3, 2, 1, or 0.

In addition to the three quantum numbers $n, \ell,$ and $k,$ connected with orbital motion, there is also the spin quantum number σ. The four numbers together specify the state of an individual electron in the atom, i.e., they represent its exact state. Instead of σ we sometimes require the total angular momentum of the electron $j = \ell \pm \frac{1}{2}$. The point is that there are two ways in which the angular momentum of individual electrons are combined to form the resultant angular momentum. In light atoms, and often in heavy ones, the orbital angular momenta are added to form the resultant angular momentum of the atom, and the spins are also added separately. This occurs when the individual orbital angular momenta interact with each other more strongly than with the electron spins. The common effect of all the electrons on the given electron is stronger than the action of the magnetic field associated with its spin. This couples the orbital motions of the electrons to each other (while the orbital motion of each electron is not coupled to its spin). Since in this case the quantum number j is unsatisfactory we have to use the spin quantum number σ. If, on the other hand, the spin-orbit interaction of each electron is large (as often occurs in heavy atoms), we have to add the values of j of the individual electrons to get the total angular momentum J of the atom.

The basic problem in the theory of many-electron atoms is to explain Mendeleyev's periodic table by comparing it with the general principles of quantum mechanics. For this it is sufficient to specify the state of the atom by means of the quantum numbers of the individual electrons. The fundamental rule is: there cannot be more than one electron in an atom with the same four quantum numbers. This is called the Pauli exclusion principle. It is important to note that the set of four numbers includes the spin quantum number. In this sense, the spin itself is a stronger indication of the general state of a many-electron system than the action of its magnetic field. The word "exclusion" is used to indicate that a state with given four quantum numbers in an atom can be occupied by only one electron.

Indeed the exclusion principle holds for all particles with half-integral spin. This follows from relativistic quantum mechanics (Chapter Eight). In the meantime we shall adopt Pauli's principle as a postulate. It is as rigorous, however, as the law of conservation of energy. The Pauli exclusion principle and the classification of the states of individual electrons by their quantum numbers are quite sufficient for a complete interpretation of the periodic system.

The first and lightest element, hydrogen, has only one electron, which moves in the field of a proton. The proton and electron attract each other according to the inverse square low. In this, and only in this simple case does the energy depend solely on the principal quantum number. A profound connection exists between this result of quantum mechanics and the fact that in classical mechanics the trajectories of particles in an inverse-square field are closed curves (in fact, ellipses). This is one of the manifestations of the correspondence principle that we cannot prove here, since unfortunately higher mathematics would be required. Indeed, the analogous problem in Newtonian mechanics also requires the use of calculus, invented by Newton to solve this problem.* In quantum mechanics the energy of an electron moving in the Coulomb field of the nucleus is inversely proportional to the square of the principal quantum number n, but does not depend on ℓ and n_r separately.

The potential energy curve for Coulomb forces is shown in Figure 21. Zero potential energy is reached at an infinite distance from the nucleus; i.e., the curve lies entirely in the negative region. It is now easy to understand that an electron bound in an atom must possess negative total energy. In fact any horizontal line representing an energy level will cut the potential energy curve. Beyond the point of intersection, the potential energy will be greater than the total energy, since the kinetic energy, formally speaking, will be negative. In quantum mechanics this means that the wave function in the corresponding region is attenuated (Chapter Three). Consequently, the electron cannot escape from the atom as it is bound to it in discrete states. The total energy is inversely proportional to the square of the principal quantum number, which cannot be less than unity (remember $n = n_r + \ell + 1$ and the least values of ℓ and n_r are zero). Furthermore, it is clear that $-1/1^2 < -1/2^2 < -1/3^2 \ldots$ and the lowest value of energy, or ground-state energy, of the hydrogen atom corresponds to $n = 1$.

How many electrons in any atom can have $n = 1$? For if $n = 1$, ℓ must be zero. Then $k = 0$ since ℓ is the greatest value of k. Only the spin quantum number takes two values $\sigma = \pm\frac{1}{2}$. Thus for $n = 1$, there are only two sets of quantum num-

* Recently Feyhman was able to prove without using calculus that planets move in elliptical orbits. His reasoning, however, is by no means simple.

bers: 1, 0, 0, $\frac{1}{2}$ and 1, 0, 0, $-\frac{1}{2}$. By Pauli's principle, not more than one electron can be in each of these states. It follows that an atom can contain at most two electrons with $n = 1$.

In the atom of helium, the next element after hydrogen, there are just two electrons. These assume the two possible states with $n = 1$. The energy of these states is very different from that of states with $n = 2$. A fairly large amount of energy, approximately 20 eV, is required to transfer an electron in the helium atom from the ground state with $n = 1$ into the next state with $n = 2$. The energy required to move a system out of a given state is a measure of the stability of that state. A system of two electrons with $n = 1$ therefore has a very stable configuration. We say that these two electrons occupy the K shell. Every atom from helium on has a full K shell. In the old theory of Bohr, this property of the helium configuration could not be explained.

The stability of the K shell of the helium atom is the reason for its very weak reactivity with other atoms, whether they be atoms of helium or of any other element. Helium does not form chemical compounds and liquefies only at very low temperatures. The latter property is due to the very slight attraction that helium atoms have for each other. The weakness of this attraction is connected with the stability of the electron configuration. Neutral atoms act on other atoms only when they are somewhat polarized, i.e., when the electron shells are displaced with respect to the nucleus. This displacement and deformation causes the resultant negative charge of the electrons in the shells not to coincide with the positive charge of the nucleus. The atomic system is then no longer centrally symmetric and is capable of entering into electrical interactions resembling the actions of magnets. Owing to quantum effects these electrical forces decrease more rapidly with distance than do the magnetic effects. They are exceptionally small in helium because of the stability of the K shell, which is difficult to deform. Thermal motion impedes the transition of the weakly interacting atoms into the liquid state until very low temperatures are reached.

On account of this chemical inertness, helium is called an *inert* gas, or else a *noble* gas, by analogy with noble metals, which form chemical compounds far less readily than "base" elements.

After helium comes lithium. The K shell with $n = 1$ is now completely filled, and the L shell with $n = 2$ starts to fill up. For $n = 2$, ℓ can take two values: $\ell = 0$ and $\ell = 1$. If $\ell = 0$, then $k = 0$, so that, as in the K shell, there are two states corresponding to $\sigma = \pm\frac{1}{2}$. If $\ell = 1$, k can take three values: 1, 0, -1; but for each value of k there are two values of σ, giving six states. Thus in the L shell there are in all $2 + 6 = 8$ states. These eight states correspond exactly to the first period of Mendeleyev's periodic table.

In lithium only one of the eight possible states is occupied with $n = 2$, $\ell = 0$. The binding energy of such an electron is very much less than that of the K electrons. There are two reasons for this. Firstly, the principal quantum number is twice as great. If the same law as in the hydrogen atom applied, the bond energy would be four times less than for $n = 1$; but in addition to this, the more strongly bound K electrons move closer to the nucleus—this may be easily verified by following the horizontal line in Figure 21. The lower this energy line is drawn, the more quickly the wave function is attenuated in going away from the nucleus, so that close to the nucleus the total energy is less than the potential energy. Hence the K electrons screen the charge of the nucleus from the L electron, and it is bound more weakly than one would expect for a hydrogen-type atom. The L electron of the lithium atom is also weakly bound and is considerably further from the nucleus, on the average, than the K electrons.

This is responsible for the great chemical activity of lithium, which loses its outer electron to other atoms very easily. This property is characteristic of the alkali metals, of which lithium is the first. We shall now show how to describe the states of all its electrons. We have already said that the states corresponding to $\ell = 0$, 1, 2, and 3 are called the *s, p, d,* and *f* states. The principal quantum number is put in front of the letter so that in hydrogen there is a 1*s* electron and in helium there are two such electrons. The number of electrons is denoted symbolically by an exponent in the spectroscopic notation: hydrogen 1*s*, helium $(1s)^2$, lithium $(1s)^2 2s$.

In beryllium, which comes after lithium, the configuration is $(1s)^2 (2s)^2$. By Pauli's principle, no more than two electrons may be found in the 1*s* and 2*s* states; but we must not think that beryllium has a stable shell of the helium type. The reason is that the energy of a 2*s* electron is not very different from that of a 2*p* electron. Although the field acting on an electron in a beryllium atom is not strictly a Coulomb one, the difference from a Coulomb field is still not very large since the field of all the other electrons is added to the field of the nucleus. Hence the energy depends far more on the principal quantum number *n* than on the azimuthal number ℓ. It is very easy to pass from the 2*s* state into the 2*p* state, so that beryllium is not in the least like an inert gas. It is, of course, a metal.

The first period begins with lithium and ends with neon, in which the shell with principal quantum number $n = 2$ is filled. Neon, whose electronic configuration is $(1s)^2 (2s)^2 (2p)^6$, is an inert gas. Hence the next electron must go into the shell with $n = 3$, and will also be weakly bound, like the electron in lithium. The element after neon is in fact the alkali metal sodium, which begins the second period of Mendeleyev's system. For each element in the first period there is a corresponding element in the second period in which the electrons in the last shell (which is still incomplete) have $n = 3$ instead of $n = 2$. Thus carbon has the electronic configuration $(1s)^2 (2s)^2 (2p)^2$, and silicon, which has similar chemical properties, has the structure $(1s)^2 (2s)^2 (2p)^6 (3s)^2 (3p)^2$.

When $n = 3$ the azimuthal quantum number may take the three values 0, 1, and 2. For $\ell = 0$ and 1 there are eight states; for $\ell = 2$ there are ten states, since for $\ell = 2$, k may take the five values 2, 1, 0, -1, and -2, and there are two values of σ for each k. However, the second period is completed with $\ell = 1$ only; i.e., in this period only $3s$ and $3p$ electrons occur. The inert gas argon has the configuration $(1s)^2(2s)^2(2p)^6$ $(3s)^2(3p)^6$. Why is this configuration so stable? Why does the $3d$ subshell not start to fill up immediately after the $3p$ state? It turns out that the $3d$ state differs considerably in energy from the $3p$ state. The dependence of the energy on the azimuthal quantum number is now beginning to make its effect felt.

Let us now consider the physical reasons for this. Firstly, the inner shells of elements in the second period contain enough electrons so that the field acting on the electrons in the outer shells is very different from a Coulomb field. The effect of the azimuthal quantum number on the energy now becomes comparable with the effect of the principal quantum number.

Let us clarify the reason for this. The centrifugal force mv^2/r may be rewritten as $(mvr)^2/mr^3$ if the numerator and the denominator are multiplied by mr^2. But mvr is the angular momentum, M, so that the centrifugal force is equal to M^2/mr^3. The centrifugal force is thus inversely proportional to the cube of the distance from the nucleus. We may formally introduce a potential energy, just as for other forces, and represent it by a curve. We have already seen that the potential energy curve can help us to deduce important information about the special features of motion. In Chapter Three we obtained an expression for the potential energy of forces inversely proportional to the *square* of the distance. The energy was inversely proportional to the first power of the distance. Here the potential energy corresponding to the centrifugal force is inversely proportional to the square of the distance, and in addition contains the factor $\frac{1}{2}$. If the reader wishes he may easily work this out for himself, making the necessary simple changes in the proof given in Chapter Four.

The sign of the potential energy of a centrifugal force is also easy to find; since it is a repulsive force, the energy is positive. In order to move an electron with a given angular momentum toward the nucleus, one must do work on it, i.e., increase its potential energy.

Let us now compare the potential energy associated with the centrifugal force and the potential energy of interaction between the electron and the remainder of the atom. In immediate proximity to the nucleus the energy of the Coulomb field is inversely proportional to the distance, because in this region the nucleus is not shielded by the opposite charges of the electrons. This part of the potential energy is negative. If an electron is in the *s* state, its angular momentum *M* is zero, so that the centrifugal potential energy is also zero (in classical theory this would mean that the electron moves along a straight line through the nucleus).

Unlike a classical particle, an electron with zero angular momentum does not fall into the nucleus; it has zero moment of momentum (i.e., angular momentum) and no trajectory. When the angular momentum is zero, an electron close to the nucleus experiences a pure Coulomb force. When the angular momentum is not zero, the centrifugal potential energy is always greater than the Coulomb potential energy, provided the electron is near enough to the nucleus. This is so because $1/r^2$ increases more rapidly than $-1/r$ can decrease. It follows that the potential energy curve for $\ell > 0$ always rises as r decreases.

If we consider the case of very large r, we find that screening of the nuclear charge by electrons is very important. The attractive part of the potential energy curve falls, roughly speaking, like $1/r^3$, i.e., more rapidly than the centrifugal energy. Consequently, for large values of r the centrifugal energy will once more predominate over the Coulomb energy, and the resultant energy will be positive. Somewhere among the intermediate values of r the energy will of course be negative since otherwise the potential well that is necessary for retaining the electrons would not exist. The resultant curve is shown in Figure 30.

The energy level in the well is shown as usual by a horizontal line. This is not taken as far as $r = 0$ in order to show an important property of states with $\ell > 0$. The centrifugal energy acts as a barrier preventing a particle from reaching the origin. Near the origin this force is infinitely great. This is the same barrier that prevents the earth from falling into the sun. Here again, we encounter the centrifugal force acting. However, in the case of classical motion the straight line representing the total energy is drawn up to the potential energy curve, while in quantum mechanics it is drawn to extend into the region of negative kinetic energy. A particle with $\ell > 0$ cannot reach the origin. Its wave function becomes zero at the origin, and this happens all the more the greater the value of ℓ (i.e., it behaves like r^{ℓ}). When $\ell = 0$ the electron still does not, of course, fall into the nucleus, but its wave function is not zero at the origin. It cannot get "completely" into the nucleus because this would violate the uncertainty principle. If it had a strictly defined position the uncertainty in its

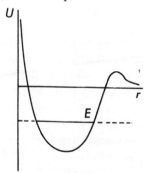

Figure 30

momentum would be so great that the Coulomb field would be unable to retain it.

We can now explain why the $3d$ subshell does not start building up in the elements immediately following argon. The $4s$ electrons, as we have just seen, approach the nucleus much more closely; the centrifugal barrier does not act on them. Hence, although the principal quantum number does increase, the electron moves closer to the nucleus and its binding energy is greater owing to the decrease in the azimuthal number. When then is the p state filled next? The point is that in the p state the square of the angular momentum is equal, as we have seen, to two, but with $\ell = 2$; i.e., in the d state, it is equal to six. In this case, k can take the values 2, 1, 0, -1, and -2. The mean square thus equals $\frac{1}{5}(2^2 + 1^2 + 0^2 + 1^2 + 2^2) = 2$, and the square of the angular momentum itself, as always, is three times the mean square of the components, or six. Hence, the centrifugal energy of the d state is three times as great as in the p state, and affects the motion of the electron to a much greater extent. In the f state the square of the angular momentum is twelve and its centrifugal energy has an even greater effect on the total energy.

The $4s$ electrons also have far less energy than the $3d$ electrons, and hence argon has the configuration of an inert gas even though its shell with $n = 3$ is not filled up; i.e., $3d$ electrons are missing. When the charge on the nucleus increases by one, the new $4s$ electron proves to be weakly bound as in the two previous alkali metals. The new element is the alkali metal potassium. It is interesting to note that although its atomic weight is less than that of argon, its nuclear charge is greater, so that potassium occurs after argon in the periodic table.

The $3d$ subshell starts to fill when the $4s$ subshell is filled. However, the $3d$ subshell does not fill in a regular manner, for suddenly, with the transition to the next element, there appears not one new electron in the $3d$ subshell but two—the second is transferred from the already filled $4s$ subshell. Then, in the next element, the $4s$ subshell is once more filled and nothing happens in the $3d$ subshell. We see from Figure 30 that the potential energy curve exhibits a "hump" on the right. This hump restricts the motion of a particle in the direction of large values of r. As a result, the $3d$ subshell is situated somewhere in the middle of the atom, essentially where the total energy is greater than the potential energy. The chemical properties of an atom are determined primarily by the outermost electrons, so that while the $3d$ subshell is being filled the chemical properties vary irregularly.

The $4f$ subshell is also filled out of turn, and is responsible for the sequence of fourteen rare-earth elements. It lies completely inside the atom (i.e., there are electrons that are external to it; their motion is unaffected by the hump of Fig. 30). The chemical properties of the rare-earth elements are very similar. Pure elements of this group or their compounds are quite difficult to separate from mixtures.

We shall not weary the reader by reconstructing the entire periodic table; we shall merely state that the system based on the quantum numbers of the individual electrons and on Pauli's principle is quite sufficient to construct and explain the whole of the periodic table.

Let us now say a few words about the nature of chemical valence. The special property of valence forces is their ability to saturate. Two atoms of hydrogen combine to form a molecule of hydrogen, but a third atom of hydrogen cannot normally combine with them. An atom of carbon can combine with no more than four hydrogen atoms. Chemists denote these components of the valence forces by dashes connecting the atomic symbols, for example: $H = H$. When very little was known about atoms, it was thought that these lines corresponded to some kind of "hooks" connecting the atoms, completely in the spirit of Lucretius' poem *De rerum natura* ("On the Nature of Things"). Nowadays, there is hardly a chemist who believes the physical reality of these hooks, even among those who do not wish to accept the ideas of quantum mechanics (of whom, happily, only very few remain).

Bohr's old quantum theory was unable to explain not only the saturation of the valence forces but even the stability of the hydrogen molecule. Electrons moving in classical orbits about two protons cannot connect them by a strong bond. Soon after the creation of quantum mechanics, Heitler and London formulated a very simple and clear approximate theory of the hydrogen molecule. This not only explained the stability and saturation of the chemical bond in the hydrogen molecule, but also made it possible to understand the general nature of the valence forces.

In particular, it was important that an explanation was found for covalent bonds, in which there is no transfer of charge from one atom to another. The nature of heteropolar bonds is a different one. For example, in NaCl the $3s$ electron of sodium, which lies outside the filled shells, is transferred to the unfilled $3p$ subshell of the chlorine atom, giving it the stable configuration of argon. In the case of hydrogen, there is no transfer of electrons from one atom of the H_2 molecule to the other. Each electron belongs simultaneously to both protons. How then does the chemical bond arise?

Let us suppose that the two protons are forcibly placed at the same point, so that a helium nucleus with atomic weight 2 (which does not occur in nature) is formed. Electrons will go into the $1s$ shell around such a nucleus without a suspicion of instability, just as they will for an actual He atom. If the protons then move apart gradually, they do not rupture this shell but only stretch it. Thus a stable hydrogen molecule is obtained. The saturation of the valence forces is therefore also understandable; in the first $1s$ shell of the helium atom of atomic weight 2 there can be only two electrons, which have opposite spins. Thus the valence lines in the $H = H$ molecule correspond to the two opposite spins—a fairly good symbolic picture replacing the hooks.

This word picture must, of course, be reinforced by calculations. Heitler and London performed such calculations beginning not with combined atoms, but with atoms an infinite distance apart. They were able to show that forces arise between these atoms as they approach each other, especially when the electron spins are antiparallel.

The idea of the mutual saturation of electron spins corresponding to the saturation of the valence forces proved to be exceptionally fruitful for understanding covalency in general. Consider, for example, how the tetravalent nature of carbon is explained. The electronic configuration of the carbon atom in the ground state is $(1s)^2(2s)^2(2p)^2$. We have seen that in light elements the $2s$ and $2p$ states differ only slightly in energy. When carbon forms a chemical compound one of the $2s$ electrons goes into the $2p$ subshell so that the configuration $(1s)^2 2s(2p)^3$ is obtained. The small amount of energy necessary for this transition is derived from chemical affinity.

It may further be shown that the spins of all three $2p$ electrons are parallel. If three electrons have identical principal, azimuthal, and spin quantum numbers, their magnetic quantum numbers must differ. For if $\ell = 1$, k can take precisely three values: 1, 0, or -1. The different magnetic quantum numbers correspond to different distributions in space of the "electron clouds." If these clouds are separated in space, the electrons will be further apart on the average than if the "clouds" were superimposed on each other. The potential energy of repulsion will then be less on the average, since it is inversely proportional to the distance between the electrons. This means that when the spins of all three $2p$ electrons are parallel, their energy is less than when two out of the three electrons have antiparallel spins. However, the lower the energy of the state, the more stable it is: the measure of stability is always the work that must be done to move the system out of the given state.

It is instructive to note that the energy of a system of electrons depends on their spin alignment, which is not at all connected with their magnetic interaction. By Pauli's principle, the alignment of the spins affects the electrons' electrostatic interaction. This is at least a thousand times greater than the magnetic interaction. Without the exclusion principle, we could not understand why the potential energy of the $2p$ electrons is least when their spins are parallel.

In the $(1s)^2 2s(2p)^3$ configuration there are four uncompensated spins, one from the $2s$ electron and three from the $2p$ electrons. Hence a carbon atom can combine with four atoms of hydrogen.

It would be almost impossible to formulate a general quantitative theory of valence, since difficulties even greater than those found in the theory of many-electron atoms would be encountered. Nevertheless, even a qualitative understanding of the nature of valency forces, based on the Heitler-London approximation and the general picture of saturated spins, is most useful.

7 Electrons in crystals

A very extensive branch of physics is devoted to studies of the very diverse properties of crystals: thermal, electrical, optical, magnetic, etc. We shall be concerned with only a few of these properties.

Just as in the theory of the atom, where we first studied the motion of an individual electron and then built up the atom as a whole (Chapters Four and Six), we shall now find it convenient to begin with a single electron in a crystal. Consider such an electron moving in the field of all the atoms in a crystal (self-consistent field). This field is due to the nuclei and all other electrons. It has the same periodicity as the crystal, and hence the first question is: how does an electron move in a three-dimensional periodic force field?

It is convenient to approach this question from two opposite points of view; one can assume that the electron is moving almost as freely as in empty space, or, on the other hand, that it is almost as bound as in the atom. Both methods give results that agree qualitatively, and hence it is reasonable to compare them with experiment in every case.

We have, in fact, already used the first approach when we considered the electron's diffraction in a crystal. Let us return to Figure 14b, and assume that de Broglie waves rather than electromagnetic waves are propagated in the crystal. Reflection occurs whenever an integral multiple of the wavelength can be fitted into the path $C_1B_2C_2$. For simplicity let us take the case where the wave is propagated at right angles to the planes, so that we have a one-dimensional picture instead of the more complicated three-dimensional one. It is immediately clear from Figure 14b that in this case the wave will be reflected whenever the wavelength equals twice the period of the lattice. For all other wavelengths the wave will pass through the lattice without reflection. The de Broglie wavelength is $\lambda = h/p$, where p is the momentum of the electron. Reflection occurs when $2a = n\lambda$. Thus waves of any length pass through the crystal except those for which $p = nh/2a$, where n is an integer.

The energy of the electrons used in the diffraction experiment is considerably greater than the bond energy of the electrons in the crystal, so that we may consider the former as almost free. We shall now extend our argument to the bound electrons in the crystal. Let us assume that they move throughout the whole crystal, almost as if they were free, but that they cannot escape from it. Their energy is given in terms of momentum by $E(p) = p^2/2m$, since $p = mv$ and $E = mv^2/2$. The graph of the energy of a free particle as a function of its momentum has the form of a parabola (Fig. 31a). Close to points where $p = nh/2a$, however, propagation of de Broglie waves through the crystal is impossible since waves reflected from successive planes of the crystal cancel each other out. Hence the true dependence of energy on momentum must be of the form shown in Figure 31b. The curve has a small discontinuity whenever $p = hn/2a$, and consists of a number of separate segments. If the projection of each segment is taken on the energy axis, we find that the electron spectrum is *almost* continuous. Some small "forbidden" regions occur, however, in the continuous spectrum. In Figure 31b, the "allowed" bands are much larger than the "forbidden."

Let us now consider the opposite approach. We assume that the electron is firmly bound in some potential well. Figure 32 represents a whole series of such wells corresponding to a simplified one-dimensional model of a crystal. The wells are

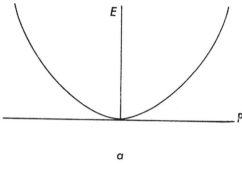

a

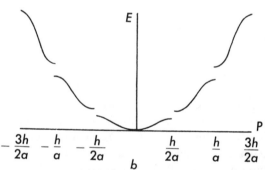

$-\dfrac{3h}{2a} \quad -\dfrac{h}{a} \quad -\dfrac{h}{2a} \qquad \dfrac{h}{2a} \quad \dfrac{h}{a} \quad \dfrac{3h}{2a}$

b

Figure 31

assumed to be infinitely deep near the nuclei, as in Figure 21. The horizontal line represents the energy level, which is the same for all the wells. The section of the curve *ABC* may be considered as a potential barrier against crossing from the first well on the left to the neighboring one. The same applies to the other wells, so that the electron cannot be considered bound in the strict sense of the word; i.e., it need not remain in a given potential well but can pass from one to the next *ad infinitum.* In this sense we can consider it to be almost free.

If the wave function in neighboring wells differs only in

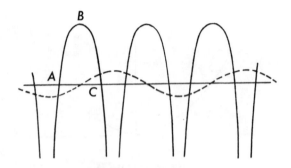

Figure 32

phase and not in amplitude, it is not attenuated as the electron passes through the crystal. Then, in spite of the series of barriers, the electron passes through the whole crystal quite freely. For this to happen the wave functions extending from the well under the barrier must be joined in such a way that their amplitude remains the same in neighboring wells. For example, such a function is shown by the broken line in Figure 32. It is in opposite phase in neighboring wells. When the wavelength is very long, the phase of the wave functions in neighboring wells is almost the same. Each wave function has its own particular energy value. For the whole phase interval (from opposite to equal) there is a corresponding interval of electron energy. We have once again reached the conclusion that there must be an interval of allowed values of the energy in which the electron can move freely through the crystal.

The higher the energy barrier separating the wells, the narrower the interval of allowed values of the energy. If the well contains not one but several levels, a sequence of allowed intervals of energy will be obtained. Each of the levels in the well corresponds to a separate electron level in the atom: the allowed values are obtained from the levels when the atoms form a crystal. We have thus reached the problem of the motion of an electron in a crystal from the other direction, i.e., by considering the electron not as almost free but as almost bound to an individual atom. However, a qualitatively similar picture is obtained (Fig. 33), except that now the allowed intervals are narrow and the forbidden ones are wide.

Let us now consider the levels of the atomic electrons shell by shell. From the K shell levels we find allowed bands that are narrow (in comparison with the forbidden bands), while from shells with higher quantum numbers we find greater intervals of allowed energies. Above the filled electron levels lie the unfilled levels where electrons occur only as a result of excitation. Since the electrons in these levels are bound more weakly, broad allowed bands separated by narrow forbidden bands are obtained from them. Sometimes the allowed bands extend so far that they partially cover each other and form a combined band. A combined band is formed in beryllium from the bands caused by the extension of the $2s$ and $2p$ levels (which, as we have said before, are fairly close together).

The transformation of the individual atomic levels into allowed bands may also be illustrated by a mechanical model. We have already said that the proper energies of an atom are analogous to the frequencies of a stretched string. If two identical strings are stretched on the same resonator and connected to each other, each frequency will be divided into two. One will correspond to the vibration of both strings in the same

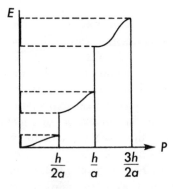

Figure 33

phase and the other to their vibrations in opposite phase. When three identical strings are stretched, the frequency is split into three, etc. (the number of frequency components is always the same as the number of strings). In the limit, when there are an infinite number of stretched strings, allowed and forbidden frequency *intervals* arise, each interval being obtained from one frequency. The weaker the coupling between the strings, the narrower are the intervals. In the limit of a very weak coupling they contract into individual frequencies.

When the energy band of a crystal is formed from a filled atomic shell, then, by Pauli's principle, all the places in it are occupied, just as in the shell. If the shell is not filled, the band, too, is only partly filled. For example, in the lattice of sodium, a band is formed from the $3s$ subshell. Sodium has only one electron in this shell; therefore only half the states that the band contains are occupied. If there are N atoms in the lattice, there could be $2N$ electrons in the band, but in fact there are only N. Since the stable state always has the least possible energy, the lower N states are occupied, and the upper N are free. In beryllium, the band obtained from the $2s$ subshell is filled, but it occurs in conjunction with the $2p$ subshell, which is free.

If an external electric field is applied to a crystal possessing an incompletely filled band, the electrons in it will accelerate and their energies will increase so that they transfer from the filled part of the band into the unfilled part. In a completely filled band there is no room for further electrons. Thus, when all the bands in the crystal are filled, an applied electric field cannot accelerate its electrons. We have therefore reached an electronic quantum-mechanical explanation of the difference between a metal and an insulator: in a metal there are one or more incompletely filled bands, while in an insulator there are none.

In hydrogen the K shell is only half filled, as it contains only one electron. Nevertheless, solid hydrogen is a dielectric and not a metal. This is because solid hydrogen is composed of molecules and not of individual atoms (see Chapter Six). Hence the molecular crystal of hydrogen is a dielectric. However, under very high pressures the crystal is transformed into an atomic crystal of higher density. According to the calculations of A. A. Abrikosov the necessary pressure would be 3 million atmospheres. Solid hydrogen should then exhibit the properties of a metal.

Although we have stated the conditions under which a crystal can conduct a current, we have not yet discussed the nature of conduction. If an electron in a metal could be accelerated without limit in an electric field, the metal would possess infinite conductivity. For any value of the field, an infinitely large current would be produced. In fact, however, to every field there corresponds a definite finite current that is directly proportional to the applied field (Ohm's law). The theory must therefore explain the *finite* conductivity of metals.

Our discussion of the free motion of an electron in a crystal referred only to an ideally regular crystal; but the electron can be reflected from any crystal irregularity, preventing it from being accelerated without limit by the electric field. Even if the crystal contained no structural irregularities or impurities its order would be disturbed by the thermal motion of the component atoms. When an electron moves in a crystal whose atoms execute thermal oscillations, it exchanges its energy with the lattice. When there is no external field the electron, on the average, acquires and gives up the same energy. When a field is applied, however, the equilibrium is upset. The electron imparts the extra energy acquired from the field to the lattice, increasing its thermal motion. This is responsible for the production of Joule heat. At absolute zero the thermal motion of the lattice ceases, and the atomic oscillations no longer impede the motion of electrons. Hence the electrical resistance of an ideal crystal must become zero. F. Bloch, the author of the modern electron theory of metals, concluded in 1930 that near absolute zero the resistance of metals tends to zero like the fifth power of the temperature.

The classical electron theory of metals was proposed by Drude at the beginning of this century, soon after the existence of the electron ceased to be a mere hypothesis. Drude regarded electrons as a kind of gas present in the crystal. It is well known that every gas, whether it is made up of individual atoms or other particles (e.g., electrons), has a specific heat of 3 cal/mole deg, which is independent of the mass of the particles.* However, in comparison with insulators, metals have no additional specific heat, and Drude's theory was unable to explain this.

In 1926 Sommerfeld pointed out that the Pauli principle had considerably changed the situation (the first impetus had in fact been provided by Fermi's work). Let us examine how this came about. Since the thermal energy per mole must equal 3 cal/mole deg, the value per electron will be proportionally smaller in accordance with the number of electrons in 1 mole, i.e., it will be 6.024×10^{23} times smaller. At a temperature of $300°K$ this gives:

$$\frac{3 \times 4 \times 10^7 \times 300}{6 \times 10^{23}} = 6 \times 10^{-14} \text{ erg}$$

For comparison with atomic quantities, we can turn this result into electron volts by dividing by 1.6×10^{-12}. This gives approximately 0.04 eV. The width of the allowed energy band is of the order of a few electron volts. Suppose that a band is only half-filled with electrons. The distance from the bottom of the band to the uppermost filled level (the so-called Fermi-level) is about 4 eV. Hence, an electron occupying a level further than 0.04 eV from the upper boundary simply cannot undergo thermal excitation; that would put it into one of the upper levels that has already been filled. In other words, a man in the middle of a crowd cannot force his way out of it, but if he is at the edge, he is, of course, able to do so. In the same way an electron with energy that is close to the up-

---

* Provided these particles are not rotating in space like rigid tops or performing internal oscillations.

permost filled level can undergo thermal excitation of 0.04 eV. For a total width of the filled part of the band equal to 4 eV, this constitutes about a hundredth of the total number of electrons. Thus Pauli's principle explains why the electrons of a metal play such a small part in its specific heat. This removes the principal difficulty of Drude's theory.

However, even the Sommerfeld-Bloch theory was for a long time unable to explain one very striking fact. As early as 1911, Kamerlingh Onnes in Leyden discovered that the resistance of certain metals suddenly became zero at a temperature several degrees above absolute zero. This phenomenon is called superconductivity. The current produced in a ring of superconducting metal by electromagnetic induction will go on flowing undiminished for an indefinitely long time, since none of the energy is dissipated as Joule heat. Superconductivity is also observed in metals containing impurities and structural imperfections, which according to Bloch's theory would retain a "residual" resistance even at absolute zero. However, imperfection does not affect superconductivity.

Superconductivity remained a mystery for more than 45 years until Bardeen, Cooper, and Schrieffer explained it. Their theory was improved by N. N. Bogolyubov. Superconductivity was explained after the discovery of the *isotope effect*. When superconductivity is studied in samples of the same metals made up of different pure isotopes, the temperature of transition into the superconducting state is found to depend somewhat on the atomic weight of the isotopes. Isotopes of heavy elements differ only in their atomic weights; their electron structure is the same. Consequently, superconductivity must be connected with some property of the crystal that is directly related to its atomic weight. This can clearly be only the thermal oscillation of the crystal. It is well known that for a given elastic force the frequency of oscillation of a body is inversely proportional to the square root of the mass. The elastic force is completely accounted for by the electronic properties, so that the entire difference between the isotopes consists of the frequency difference of their thermal oscillations due to the difference in mass. However, even after the discovery of the isotope effect the explanation of superconductivity did not follow at once.

Fröhlich observed that the thermal oscillations must lead to a special form of interaction between the electrons themselves. When we speak of the resistance of a metal we mean that the electron may either absorb energy from the thermal oscillations or else impart its energy to them. In this sense the interaction of the field of elastic oscillations in the crystal with the electron is very reminiscent of the interaction of an electromagnetic field with it. Here too the electron may absorb or radiate individual portions of energy (quanta). If one electron emits a quantum of energy and another absorbs it, this corresponds to an interaction between the electrons. The intermediate agent —the field—is, so to speak, eliminated. In empty space this agent can only be the electromagnetic field, but in the crystal there is also the field of the elastic oscillations. Fröhlich considered the interaction between the electrons transmitted by the elastic oscillations of the crystal from a theoretical point of view. He started from the fact that in different isotopes of the same element superconductivity begins at slightly different temperatures. However, he was not able to explain the phenomenon of superconductivity itself.

Theory and experiment still remained separated. It was known from experiment that the atomic weight affected the temperature of transition into the superconductivity state, and from theory that the atomic weight affected the interaction between electrons through the thermal oscillations of the lattice; but how the one was connected with the other was revealed only after the theoretical work of Bardeen, Cooper, Schrieffer, and Bogolyubov. The energy of the thermal oscillations of the lattice is absorbed and emitted by the electrons and couples electrons in pairs in which the momenta and spins are each antiparallel. This "bond" does not resemble the electron-nucleus "bond," which is due to electromagnetic forces. In the present case the Pauli principle plays an essential role. If this principle did not operate, such pairs would be unstable; they would break down and pass into the free state. Pauli's exclusion principle does not allow them to go into an unbound state if the state is already occupied by other electrons. Some additional energy must be supplied before the members of the pair can find free places in an energy band; but if energy is required to break up the pair, this means that the two electrons form a stable bound state.

This form of bond does not resemble the bond of an individual electron in a potential well. Controlled by the action of the other electrons of the system on the pair under consideration, it is a special effect that cannot be understood without Pauli's principle.

The bound state is stable against disturbances. When an external electric field is applied to the metal, all electrons, including those in bound pairs, are accelerated in the direction of the applied field. This means that although originally the pair had zero resultant momentum, the application of the field gives rise to a nonzero momentum component in the direction of the field. The bond is still intact, however, and the motion of the lattice cannot break it because it is precisely this motion that was responsible for the bond in the first place. This mechanism thus avoids the transfer of energy to the lattice and thereby removes resistance to the flow of currents. Superconductivity was, in fact, the last phenomenon in physics outside the domain of nuclear forces to remain unexplained. Now there are no such phenomena left.

In addition to metals and dielectrics, an intermediate class of substances exists: the semiconductors. Their resistance is much higher than that of metals, and at absolute zero becomes infinite, like that of insulators. Moreover, this resistance is very closely connected with the purity of the crystal. Hence it is clear that the property of semiconductivity itself must be connected somehow with the impurities in the crystal.

Usually the energy level of an impurity atom in a lattice

lies somewhat below the lower edge of an unfilled energy band. If the distance is of the order of a few hundredths of an electron volt, then, as we have already seen, an electron from the impurity atom may become detached through thermal excitation and find itself in an unfilled band. Under such conditions electrons behave as if they were free; they carry charge and turn the crystal into a conductor. Their number in the band is relatively small in comparison with the number of atoms in the crystal, because the impurity concentration is usually low. For a small number of electrons the exclusion principle cannot make its effect felt, since so few of the states in the band are occupied. The electrons may move freely from one state to another without risking a "collision" with an occupied state. This resembles Drude's classical electron theory, except that we are now dealing with semiconductors and not metals.

There is also another type of semiconductor in which the impurity has a free level a few hundredths of an electron volt above the upper edge of the filled band. The thermal motion then transfers electrons from the filled levels to the free level of the impurity, so that unfilled levels or "holes" are left. This term has received universal recognition and is used in scientific literature without quotation marks. A hole behaves in an electric field like an electron with a positive charge.

Sometimes one part of a semiconductor possesses electron conductivity and another part hole conductivity. For this to occur there must be different kinds of impurities in the respective parts. The electron type of conductivity is denoted for brevity by the letter n (negative) and the hole type by p (positive). The boundary between the regions where transition from one type to the other takes place is called an np junction.

At the np junction there must certainly be a jump in the electrostatic potential. The electrons and the holes may be considered as two "gases" which tend to fill the whole crystal. If the particles were neutral there would be no obstacle to this; but the displacement of charged particles—electrons and holes—creates an electric field acting in the opposite direction to the applied field. Suppose that the electrons lie to the left and the holes to the right. Then the field opposing the motion of the holes acts from left to right. However, since the charge on the electrons is negative, the same field repels them from right to left. This field creates a potential jump at the *np* junction.

Let us now connect the *n*-type and *p*-type semiconductor areas with an external wire, so that we have the following circuit: *n*-type semiconductor, *np* junction, *p*-type semiconductor, wire, and the *n*-type semiconductor again. If there is no external source of energy it is clear that no current can flow; otherwise we would have a perpetual motion machine creating energy out of nothing.

Let light fall on an *n*-type semiconductor and be absorbed by the electrons. If the electrons obtain sufficient energy to overcome repulsion from the *np* junction, the electric field of the *np* junction will no longer retain them. A current will flow in the circuit, its energy being provided by the incident light. This transformation of radiant energy to electrical energy is called the photoelectric effect.

In this case the conversion efficiency is fairly high, so that there is some possibility of using photoelectric devices for energy conversion. Small amounts of solar energy are already being transformed into electric energy in satellites' photocell batteries. Photoelectric devices have a wide range of application in sound films, signaling, etc.

At absolute zero there is no thermal motion, and the transfer of electrons to and from the impurities ceases. The semiconductor then becomes an insulator.

There are crystals that are intrinsically magnetized; i.e., the magnetic moments of all the atoms are aligned in the same direction. These are called ferromagnetic substances, e.g., iron, cobalt and nickel. All these elements possess unfilled 3*d* subshells, which lie within the atom (see Chapter Six). The electron spins in these shells are relatively free because the lattice has little effect on them. However, with respect to each other the spins are parallel instead of being arbitrarily aligned.

Before the advent of quantum mechanics, it was supposed that the magnetic moments tend to become parallel through the action of the magnetic forces between them; but it is easily shown that the magnetism of iron and other ferromagnetic substances cannot be explained by the magnetic interaction of the spins. Let us calculate the energy of such an interaction. The potential energy of the two magnets is equal to the product of their moments divided by the cube of the distance between them. The magnetic moment of the spin is equal to 1 Bohr magneton, i.e., 10^{-20} (CGS). The distance between the atoms in the lattice is of the order of 10^{-8} cm. Hence the energy of magnetic interaction is approximately 10^{-16} ergs. This is the energy of thermal motion at one degree above absolute zero. Since thermal energy is random, it tends to destroy all order if it is sufficiently energetic. In fact, however, iron loses its magnetic properties at a temperature of about $1000°$K. Consequently, the spin alignment is controlled by forces that in the limiting case are about 1000 times greater than the magnetic forces.

In the previous chapter we saw that there is a special kind of spin interaction that has a completely different nature. The spins are aligned in such a way that the electrical interactions between the electrons themselves (Coulomb repulsion) are minimal. In this situation both the amplitude and the phase of the wave function are important. The Coulomb repulsion is determined not only by the squares but also by the products of the wave functions of the individual electrons. But the product of the wave functions of different electrons may be of either sign, according to the signs of the multiplicands. This factor proves to be decisive for the stability of the hydrogen molecule: it gives a negative term in the total energy of the system, which compensates the positive term due to the repulsion. Since the phase of the wave function is a pure quantum-mechanical concept, this result cannot be explained with the aid of electrical analogies such as the electron-cloud model.

In the case of the hydrogen molecule, a negative term is obtained only when the spins of the electrons are antiparallel. However, it is assumed (although no one has yet proved it by direct calculation) that the repulsion between the $3d$ electrons of iron two atoms is least when the spins are parallel. Thus it is assumed that the electrostatic interaction of two iron atoms depends considerably on the alignment of their spins, i.e., of the magnetic moments. Magnetization is not the cause but an effect of the parallel alignment of the moments. Since the electrical forces are about a thousand times greater than the magnetic forces, we can understand why the magnetism of iron persists up to about $1000°K$. It would be very interesting to calculate directly the energy of the electrical interaction that aligns the spins, but because of the difficulty of obtaining an exact solution of the many-electron problem, approximate methods have to be used. Since different authors use different methods, it is not surprising that contradictory results are sometimes obtained.

A large single crystal of iron is not magnetized entirely in one direction: if it were, a great deal of energy would be necessary to establish its external magnetic field. The crystal is divided into separate layers magnetized in opposite directions, so that their external fields tend to compensate each other. If we apply an external field to such a crystal, layers with moments in the opposite direction to the field will realign, and all parts of the crystal will have a single direction of magnetization. The theory of the layered structure of ferromagnetics, formulated by Landau and Lifshits, was later verified by direct observations.

8 Quantized fields

In this chapter although we shall refer a number of times to Einstein's theory of relativity, we shall assume that the reader has not yet acquired a knowledge of this theory.

The principal difficulty in understanding Einstein's theory is that it reappraises our customary concepts of space and time. Hence there arise certain "paradoxes," which are in fact as natural as the consequences of the uncertainty principle; but we shall leave aside these consequences of the theory of relativity, which are especially difficult to grasp. For our purposes certain ideas and formulas taken from relativistic mechanics are far more important ("relativistic" was defined in Chapter Four as "in accordance with the requirements of the theory of relativity").

It is first essential to have an expression for energy in terms of momentum. We know from Chapter Seven that in Newtonian mechanics, this takes the form $E = p^2/2m_0$. In Einstein's mechanics the formula is quite different: $E = \sqrt{m_0^2 c^4 + c^2 p^2}$, where c is the velocity of light and m_0 is the mass at rest. Although at first glance it would seem that these two formulas have nothing in common, this is in fact not so. Let us investigate how Einstein's formula differs from Newton's.

When $p = 0$ (i.e., when the particle is at rest) we have $E_0 = m_0 c^2$. The relationship between the energy and mass of a particle at rest is completely foreign to Newtonian mechanics. The quantity $m_0 c^2$ is called the *rest energy* of the particle, and is of vital importance in the various transformations of particles studied in nuclear physics and the physics of elementary particles. We will now show that the energy of a particle moving *slowly* in comparison with the velocity of light consists of the rest energy E_o and an additional term that is the same as the Newtonian expression for the kinetic energy. We denote this by T, so that $E = E_o + T = m_o c^2 + T$. Squaring both sides of this expression, we have:

$$E^2 = m_o^2 c^4 + 2m_o c^2 T + T^2$$

Suppose, for example, that the velocity of the particle is a hundredth part of the velocity of light. The kinetic energy $\frac{1}{2} m_o v^2$ is then a $1/20,000$ part of the rest energy: $T/E_o = \frac{1}{2} \times 10^{-4}$. The square of the kinetic energy will equal $1/(4 \cdot 10^8)$ of the square of the rest energy. Hence we may ignore it in the expression for E^2, and we are left with only $E^2 = m_o^2 c^4 + 2m_o c^2 T$; but this expression by the fundamental formula equals $m_o^2 c^4 + c^2 p^2$. Canceling $m_o^2 c^4$ on both sides and dividing through by $2m_o c^2$ we obtain simply $T = p^2/2m_o$, which must hold for slowly moving particles. Thus for small velocities the formulas of Einstein's mechanics reduce to the Newtonian formulas, provided that no transformation of particles takes place.

It is even more interesting to see how the energy behaves when the momentum is very large. The square of the rest energy makes a smaller and smaller contribution (in comparison with $c^2 p^2$) to the term under the square root. In the limit we are left with only $c^2 p^2$, and obtain simply $E = cp$. Such a particle is said to be ultrarelativistic. It is clear from the expression for the energy that the particle may have no rest mass at all. Thus Einstein's mechanics does not exclude the existence of particles with zero rest mass. If the reader is accustomed to thinking that mass represents the "quantity of matter," he must drop this idea completely. It is more correct to define the mass of a particle as its rest energy divided by the square of the velocity of light, or, taking c as the unit of velocity, simply as the rest energy. Some particles have no rest energy. We shall see later what these particles are.

Having discussed the formulas, we shall now turn to the general concepts of the matter (from which in fact the formulas emerge).

As we know, Newtonian mechanics is based on the idea of action at a distance. The best example of this is the law of gravity: two bodies attract each other with a force inversely proportional to the square of the distance between them. If one of the bodies is displaced even a small distance, the other immediately "becomes aware of it" through the change in the gravitional force, however far away the first body may be. This assertion, if we think about it, is extremely strange, and we use it without stopping to think only through force of habit.

When we consider the motion of an electron in an atom, we repeatedly use Coulomb's law, which is outwardly very similar to the law of Newton. In fact all electromagnetic interactions are propagated with the same fundamental (and finite) velocity, c; but if the charges are moving sufficiently slowly, the electromagnetic field will always be able to catch up with them so quickly that their action will seem to be transmitted instantaneously. Hence we have the likeness between Coulomb's law and the law of gravity. The electron in a hydrogen atom has a velocity of the order of one hundredth of the velocity of light. It may therefore be assumed that its kinetic energy is related to the momentum by the Newtonian relationship $E = p^2/2m_0$. Since the electron is moving slowly we may also assume that all electromagnetic actions are propagated instantaneously. The theory of relativity states that both these simplifications are directly connected with each other. (Einstein also created an exact theory of gravitation in which there is no action at a distance; it is called the general theory of relativity. We are not concerned with that here.)

Thus the electromagnetic forces are always propagated from point to point by short-range action. These ideas, first expressed by Faraday and developed by Maxwell, later led to the creation of the theory of relativity. It denies action at a distance. Interaction in relativity is always due to some sort of propagation process. In order for an electromagnetic interaction to take place between two charges, one of them must radiate a wave and the other must absorb it. What happens before the radiated charge "receives the signal"? To what does the radiated wave belong? Evidently, to the electromagnetic field itself.

Hence we cannot discuss a system of charges with relative velocity close to the velocity of light by using the concept of an instantaneously transmitted force, since otherwise all conservation laws would break down. It would thus seem that we have to regard the electromagnetic field *as part of the mechanical system*.

However, an electromagnetic field as a mechanical object is an unfamiliar idea. It resembles a continuous medium, a gas or a liquid, more than a system of separate points. In order to prescribe the state of the electromagnetic field at a given time, we must define it at every point of space; but the points of space form a continuous, not a discrete set, and it is impossible to enumerate them like the points of a mechanical system.

There exists, however, one very simple approach to the problem, based on a direct analogy between the equations of electrodynamics and the equations describing the oscillations of a string. The two belong to the same class; they describe oscillatory motion. We have remarked several times that there is a mathematical similarity between various kinds of physical oscillations.

Any arbitrary oscillation of a string may be resolved into individual simple harmonic oscillations. Each of these is characterized by a definite number of nodes. In other words, any given oscillation of a string is a sum of oscillations without nodes, with one node, with two nodes, etc. The points of the string itself form a continuous set and cannot be enumerated; but the oscillations are enumerated very simply by the number of nodes: fundamental, first harmonic, second harmonic, etc. Each oscillation is characterized by its own amplitude and phase, and most important, takes place completely independently of the others.

Due to the similarity between the equations, the electromagnetic field may also be represented by a set of individual oscillations that are independent of each other. Electromagnetic oscillations in a circuit consisting of a capacitance and an inductance are well known to everyone, but a field in empty space can also undergo harmonic oscillations.

The oscillations in a circuit are often compared to mechanical oscillations: the self-inductance is analogous to a mass and the capacity to an elastic force. This comparison of electromagnetic and mechanical oscillation shows that the laws governing them are identical. The laws governing the behavior of an individual harmonic oscillation of an electromagnetic field in empty space are also the same.

Quantum mechanics is completely analogous in one respect to classical mechanics: it studies laws of motion without concerning itself with what it is that moves. In particular, we can use quantum mechanics for a harmonic oscillation irrespective of what it is that is oscillating: an atom in a molecule or an electromagnetic field in empty space. The possible values of the energy are already known to us. They are $h\nu(n + \frac{1}{2})$ where ν is the frequency of the oscillations and n is an integer. The energy of zero-point oscillations is not usually taken into account so that n indicates the number of quanta with a given energy. Each quantum has energy $h\nu$. If the energy of the field varies (e.g., if some of it is given to an atom) then the change is most definitely discrete. Quanta are absorbed (or radiated) only in whole numbers, usually one quantum of a given frequency at a time. This follows from the laws of quantum mechanics as applied to electromagnetic oscillations.

Historically the concept of quantization of the electromagnetic field was developed in a different way. The first steps in this direction were taken by Planck in 1900, but quantum mechanics proper did not develop for another 25 years. A simple development of the kind we have just given was not possible in 1900. It is all the more enlightening, therefore, to follow the historical development of an idea that led to a major revolution in physics.

Consider a closed cavity inside a furnace whose walls radiate energy into the cavity. After a time thermal equilibrium will be established between the wall and the radiation: every square centimeter of the surface will absorb and emit equal amounts of energy per unit time per unit frequency range. The question is: what is the energy of the radiation in the cavity?

We have already said that an electromagnetic field can always be divided up into a number of individual harmonic oscillations. It is sufficient to calculate the energy of an individual oscillation and then sum over all such oscillations. This yields the energy of the field. What, however, was the position before Planck?

The thermal energy of a free particle is 3 cal/mole deg. An oscillating particle, unlike a free one, will also have potential energy that is equal on the average to the kinetic energy. Hence the thermal energy is 6 cal/mole deg, but the number of oscillations is infinite. Thus we have obtained a contradiction and clearly the result that the energy of radiation in thermal equilibrium with a substance is infinitely great must be erroneous.

How can we overcome this difficulty? Planck proposed that the radiation is emitted in finite portions of energy $h\nu$. From this proposition Planck deduced the formula for the energy distribution in the radiation and obtained excellent agreement with experiment. The energy of radiation in his theory is finite. It is impossible to overestimate the daring of Planck's hypothesis. Before his time it was assumed that all changes in physical quantities must take place smoothly ("nature makes no jumps"); but this "axiom" proved to be incorrect or, rather, of limited application.

The next important step after Planck was made by Einstein. It was known that when the surface of a metal was illuminated, it emitted electrons. Experiment shows that the energy of these electrons depends only on the frequency of the incident light and not on its intensity. From the classical point of view, this is inexplicable: the intensity characterizes the amplitude of the oscillations in the light wave. One would expect that the greater the amplitude of the oscillations the more strongly the electron would be affected and the greater would be its velocity of emission.

The true state of affairs was explained very simply by Einstein on the basis of Planck's hypothesis. If the energy of a quantum is hv, and the work needed to force an electron out of the metal is w, the kinetic energy of the emerging electron will be $hv - w$. This relationship between the frequency of light and the energy of the electron is in fact independent of the intensity of the incident radiation. This has been confirmed by experiment.

Einstein also realized that quantization was not merely a property of radiation but a general property of all oscillations, for example, the oscillations of atoms in crystals. Before Einstein's work it was generally believed that the energy per oscillatory mode in a crystal was 6 cal/mole deg, and this led to the law of Dulong and Petit stating that the specific heat of all elements in the crystalline state should be the same. Actually, this law is not satisfied for a number of elements. For example, the specific heat of diamond, i.e., crystalline carbon, is much less than predicted by the Dulong-Petit law. Einstein established that at a given temperature quanta of energy hv will not be excited in the crystal if hv is appreciably greater than the thermal excitation energy. Thermal motion is not distributed over all oscillation modes of the crystal but is confined to the low-frequency range. At low frequencies each mode has the energy prescribed by Dulong and Petit, but at higher frequencies there is less energy, and the crystal as a whole thus receives less. This explains the departure from the law of

Dulong and Petit. Einstein's theory was extended by Debye and in this modified form is in excellent agreement with experiment.

So far we have spoken only about the energy of a quantum; but the electromagnetic field always possesses momentum: if we have to consider it as a mechanical system, then we must also formulate the laws of motion for it. The expression for the momentum of the electrodynamic field was obtained by Maxwell, the creator of electrodynamics. The momentum of an electromagnetic wave is equal to its energy divided by the velocity of light. When a wave strikes a wall, it transmits its momentum to it. The momentum transmitted to the surface is perceived as a pressure. This was observed by Lebedev in 1900.

However, since the electromagnetic field possesses momentum, then by Einstein's theory the momentum of a photon must be equal to the energy divided by the velocity of light, as in the case of an electromagnetic wave. The relationship $E = cp$ refers to an ultrarelativistic particle for which m_0c is much less than p. In the case of a photon, this relation is satisfied for all frequencies, i.e., for all p. Consequently, the rest mass of a photon is identically equal to zero. (It is sometimes said that the mass of a photon equals its energy divided by the square of the velocity of light. This quantity has the *dimensions* but not all the properties of mass.)

In fact the energy of a photon is proportional to its frequency. However, frequency is a relative quantity. If one moves toward a ray of light it increases, and if one moves in the direction of the ray it decreases (Doppler effect). This will also apply to a photon's energy or to that of any particle. The energy characterizes not only the photon itself, but also the motion of the observer. Hence the definition of mass in terms of the energy of the photon does not describe the photon itself. The only true definition of rest mass is that contained in the relationship $E = \sqrt{m_0^2c^4 + c^2p^2}$, i.e., in terms of energy and momentum simultaneously. If the observer is moving relative to the particle, m_o will always be the same, although both E and p may vary. Obviously, in this case m_o describes the particle itself; but in this definition the rest mass of the photon is strictly equal to zero.

The existence of the momentum of a single photon was confirmed experimentally by Compton in 1913. He observed the scattering of X rays by electrons. If this is considered according to the laws of classical electrodynamics, the argument would run as follows: the wave strikes the electron, makes it oscillate, and compels it in its turn to radiate. Since the oscillations of the electron are in phase with the incident wave, it must radiate with the same frequency. Compton showed that in fact the frequency of the scattered radiation is always less than the incident frequency, and this difference is greater as the angle of scattering increases.

Furthermore, the relationship between the frequency and the angle of scattering may be obtained immediately if the laws governing the collision of two elastic spheres are applied. One "sphere" is the particle and the other is the photon. The only difference is that the relationship between the momentum and the energy is not $E = p^2/2m_o$ as in the case of billiard balls, but $E = \sqrt{m_o^2 c^4 + c^2 p^2}$ for the electron and $E = cp$ for the photon. The greater the angle of scattering of the photon, the more energy it imparts to the electron. Thus the energy of the photon is reduced; i.e., its frequency is lower.

Compton's formula for the reduction in the frequency includes the ratio $h\nu/m_o c^2$. This is the ratio of the energy of the photon and the rest energy of the electron. The greater this ratio, the stronger the effect. This is the reason why the effect is appreciable for X rays but negligible for visible light.

The expression $p = h\nu/c$ agrees with de Broglie's general relationship. In fact, of course, the frequency is equal to the velocity of light divided by the wavelength. Substituting this into the expression for the momentum we obtain $p = h/\lambda$, or conversely $\lambda = h/p$. This was actually de Broglie's starting point when he deduced the same relationship for particles. Diffraction of electrons confirmed his hypothesis.

In Chapter Three we discussed the possibility of measuring the position of an electron in an atom with the aid of another, faster electron having a shorter de Broglie wavelength. The same argument may be repeated for X rays. An X-ray photon of short wavelength will transmit to the target electron an uncontrollable amount of momentum, just like a fast electron. A photon of ordinary light is not suitable for the exact measurement of the position of an electron in the atom: the wavelength of visible light is about 10,000 times greater than the radius of an atom. On the other hand, a photon with wavelength smaller than the radius of the atom proves to be as rough a measuring instrument as a high-energy electron.

Although visible light also exhibits quantum properties, these are usually manifested in energy and not in a momentum relationship. Bohr's relationship

$$\nu = \frac{E_1 - E_2}{h}$$

is always satisfied when an atom emits visible radiation. In conclusion, we must indicate the place of the light quantum (photon) in the general system of quantum mechanics, and stress its similarities and dissimilarities to the electron as a quantum-mechanical particle.

Firstly, they both possess exactly the same degree of physical reality. This need not be stated at all, but the reader might mistakenly think that the electron exists "by itself" and that the photon is somehow deduced from the wave laws of electrodynamics. The corpuscular properties of light and the wave properties of electrons cannot be "deduced." They appear as experimental facts from which the laws of quantum mechanics follow. There is a difference between the photon and the electron, which will be explained later. This does not present any doubts as to the reality of the photon, which is clearly revealed by experiment.

The principal difference between the photon and the electron is that the photon is not affected by the Pauli exclusion principle. The reason why Pauli's principle is so necessary for the electron will be explained in the following chapter. This will not apply to photons; there may be any number of photons in a given state.

A large number of photons all moving in one direction and all with the same frequency and almost the same phase (without the phase there would be no wavemotion concepts!) will be perceived as a classical electromagnetic wave with the same frequency and direction. The concept of the electromagnetic wave remains even in the limiting case of classical mechanics. This means that general wave properties such as diffraction will be conserved even in the classical case; quantum mechanics gives a deeper understanding of these processes but does not have to demonstrate their very possibility, as it must in the case of electrons.

We should not consider the classical wave amplitude as being identical to the wave function of the photon itself. The former amplitude determines the energy of the electromagnetic field. However, the relationship between the energy and the number of photons involves the frequency; the energy of a photon is proportional to its frequency. Frequency, on the other hand, is a relative quantity that depends on the observer. It follows that the probability of finding a photon at a given point of space will always depend on the state of the observer, as does the observed frequency itself. A photon is always somewhat "smeared" in space and cannot be localized exactly in any experiment, even at the price of knowing its momentum only inexactly.

The wave function of an electron corresponds in the classical limit to nothing at all, since only one electron may be found in each state. Here, the transition to the classical theory means that the wave properties of motion are excluded. The possibility or impossibility of this transition follows from the uncertainty relationships for momentum and position, under the special conditions of the motion under consideration.

We may observe another difference between the electron and the photon: the photon can be absorbed or radiated, but the electron cannot. This is partly because the electron is a charged particle, and electric charges must satisfy a very strict conservation law. However, if we speak about the electron itself and not about its charge, this difference is only noticeable in the nonrelativistic limit. In the theory of relativity the position is quite different. With proper compensation of the charge by other particles, the number of electrons may also vary. This will be considered in the following chapter.

9 Dirac's theory

The quantum theory of the electromagnetic field is fundamentally relativistic: the energy of a photon is connected with its momentum. Here there cannot be a nonrelativistic limiting case since the rest mass of a photon is identically equal to zero. This property can only be exhibited by particles moving with the velocity of light, a condition fulfilled by photons.

Because an electron possesses finite rest mass an electron's mechanics permit a nonrelativistic limit. Indeed, Schrödinger's quantum mechanics, founded on the relationship $E = p^2/2m_o$, corresponds to this limit.

However, the conditions under which the nonrelativistic wave equation is applicable are by no means always satisfied. We have seen that in heavy atoms the ratio of the electron velocity to the velocity of light may reach 0.6. This fact alone instigated a search for a relativistic wave equation soon after Schrödinger's work. The first such equation was based on the formula $E^2 = m_o^2 c^4 + c^2 p^2$. However, this generalization was inadequate for the electron since it did not take spin into account. The magnetic interaction of the spin with the orbit is a relativistic effect and hence must be included automatically in any wave equation that is in accordance with the theory of relativity. An equation that does not take the spin of the electron into account cannot describe its motion in the relativistic region.

In 1928 Dirac proposed an equation that corresponds not

numerically but symbolically to the extraction of the square root in the formula $E = \sqrt{m_0^2 c^4 + c^2 p^2}$. The electron spin must be used in this operation. Thus the spin is intimately associated with the orbital motion of the electron to which the formula $E = \sqrt{m_0^2 c^4 + c^2 p^2}$ refers. The beauty of the Dirac theory cannot be conveyed in words without formulas, any more than a musical composition can without notes or sounds.

Dirac's equation yielded very much more than, probably, even he expected at first. The most interesting and unexpected results, when first obtained, appeared to present insurmountable difficulties.

We have already said that Dirac used his own special method to extract the square root of the sum $m_0^2 c^4 + c^2 p^2$; but the root always has two signs. In nonquantum theory this presents no problem, because $E = \pm \sqrt{m_0^2 c^4 + c^2 p^2}$, it is clear that the energy is always greater than $+m_0 c^2$ or less than $-m_0 c^2$, but cannot lie between $+mc^2$ and $-mc^2$. Since all quantities change continuously in classical mechanics, positive energy cannot become negative, for it would then have to cross the "forbidden" interval of $2m_0 c^2$ (Fig. 34).

In quantum mechanics the energy can change by jumps. An electron emitting a photon can jump from a state of positive energy to a state of negative energy, and since the latter has no lower bound, it will "fall" lower and lower. Thus all electrons would soon "drop" into a state of infinite negative energy. This, as we know, does not occur.

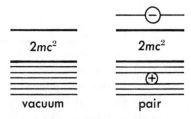

Figure 34

In order to avoid this difficulty, Dirac made a fundamental assumption. He proposed that all the negative energy states were already filled with electrons. Everything that actually happens takes place against a "background" of filled states. If the electrons obey the Pauli exclusion principle, not a single electron can pass from the states with positive energy into these filled states, and none of the electrons with negative energy can move any further down.

At first it seems that the way out proposed by Dirac is purely verbal. How can we prove that all states with negative energy are already filled by electrons?

To prove this it is sufficient to remove one electron from a negative energy state and transfer it to a positive energy state where there are as many free places as we wish. In the positive energy state it easily moves further up by absorbing a photon. Then among all the filled states there will remain one unfilled level or hole. We have already considered the properties of holes in our discussion of the conductivity of certain semiconductors. Historically, it is true, the ideas on hole conductivity were formulated by analogy to Dirac's holes. In both cases the unfilled electron level among all the filled ones behaves as if it were an electron with a positive charge.

In all other respects it behaves like an ordinary electron as long as no ordinary electron happens to meet it. When they do meet, the electron may be transferred to the unfilled level, which corresponds to the positive electron, and the excess energy will be transmitted to the electromagnetic field. Dirac used this theory to calculate probabilities of the forward and reverse processes: the creation of a positive electron and its "annihilation" by a negative electron. However, at that time, in 1930, positive electrons had not been discovered, principally because no one had thought of looking for them. The opinion of the majority of theoreticians about Dirac's theory was, to put it mildly, distrustful. The position changed radically when, in 1933, Anderson discovered the positive electron, or positron, in cosmic rays. Soon the positron was observed also in the beta decay of radioactive elements. Today the positron is a familiar particle in physical and even in chemical laboratories.

Dirac had not only predicted a new particle and worked out all its properties in advance—an outstanding event in the history of physics—but also he introduced a completely new concept into science: the concept of antiparticles. For the electron, the antiparticle is the positron. When they meet they annihilate each other with the total destruction of their rest mass. To express it more accurately, their total energy, including the rest energy, is transformed into the energy of the electromagnetic field. Without introducing any gross errors we may say briefly that their mass is converted into the energy of the electromagnetic field.

Later it was found that the concept of antiparticles is considerably wider than Dirac had at first proposed. Pauli and Weisskopf showed that a charged particle that does not obey the Pauli principle may also possess an antiparticle. At present one such particle-antiparticle pair is well known: the positive and negative pi mesons; but it makes no difference which is considered the particle and which the antiparticle, for in this sense their theory is completely symmetrical. Dirac's theory of the positron is equally symmetrical. Although to start with we spoke of levels filled by negative electrons with negative energy, and thus reduced the positron to a hole, nothing would be changed in our argument about the Dirac theory if we considered the electron as a hole in the negative energy levels filled by positrons. The fact that in our world electrons clearly predominate over the positrons (which are rare visitors) is not reflected in Dirac's theory. This is one of the problems to be solved by the science of the universe as a whole.

If we exclude the neutral pi-zero meson and the photon, every particle has its antiparticle. They have all now been discovered experimentally. As far as the first two are concerned, they both coincide with their own antiparticles. On reaching an antiuniverse composed of antiparticles (perhaps in reality in some distant galaxies) photons and pi-zero mesons would remain the same. It would be utterly disastrous to come into contact with an antiuniverse, for everything concerned would be transformed almost instantaneously into a cloud of mesons, and within a few millionths of a second (owing to meson decay) into electrons, positrons, and neutrinos. Whether these particles would in turn annihilate each other, or whether they would be scattered in space before this could happen, is of no real importance for us.

The existence of antiparticles reveals a fundamental property of relativistic quantum theory; i.e., the total number of particles is not a constant of motion. Dirac's equation as applied to an *individual* electron is only an approximation and sometimes cannot explain the actual phenomena. In addition to the given electron we must consider all the electron-positron pairs to which it might give rise *if* it had sufficient energy, and all the photons that it might radiate or absorb. Since the expression "if" allows any value of the energy, this means that we have to consider the infinite set of all the electrons and positrons in the universe and every electromagnetic field that exists or could exist.

The problem of considering such an enormous set of entities may seem insurmountable. In fact the electron does not generate a pair immediately but first emits a photon. The electron and the photon do not interact very strongly with each other. We already know that the measure of their interaction is the constant $2\pi e^2/hc = 1/137$, which is small in comparison with unity. This means that the electron usually reacts with one photon. Interactions with more than one photon at a time lead to only a small correction. The method of calculating such corrections has been thoroughly worked out.

The complicated interactions of electrons with the electromagnetic field lead only to small corrections. These corrections, however, are sometimes of great theoretical interest. In Chapter Six we stated that the energy of the electron in a hydrogen atom depends only on the principal quantum number. This follows from Schrödinger's nonrelativistic wave equation. Dirac's relativistic equation leads to a different result: the energy levels of the electron possess a fine structure and depend not only on the principal quantum number n but also on the total angular momentum of the electron, i.e., on the sum of the orbital and spin angular momenta of the electron. Since $j = \ell \pm \frac{1}{2}$, then conversely $\ell = j \pm \frac{1}{2}$. Let us now examine the $2s$ and $2p$ levels. The first of these has $\ell = 0$, so that its total angular momentum is simply equal to the spin, in this case $\frac{1}{2}$. The value of j is written as a subscript to the term* symbol; hence in the $2s$ state there can be only the $2s_{\frac{1}{2}}$ level. In the p state we can have $j = 3/2$ or $j = 1/2$. Of these, the $2p_{\frac{1}{2}}$ level has the same principal quantum number 2 and the same angular momentum $j = \frac{1}{2}$ as does the $2s_{\frac{1}{2}}$ shell; i.e., according to Dirac's theory they must possess the same energy. However, this theory takes into account only the individual electron and the Coulomb field of the nucleus in which it moves.

Spectroscopists have suspected for a long time that the $2s_{\frac{1}{2}}$ and $2p_{\frac{1}{2}}$ states in the hydrogen atom did not coincide, but could not prove this experimentally. It has been shown in microwave spectroscopy that the $2s_{\frac{1}{2}}$ level differs from the $2p_{\frac{1}{2}}$ level by 4×10^{-6} eV.

Every well-established discrepancy between theory and experiment must be explained. In the given case there is a completely quantitative explanation. Firstly, we must not assert that the electron exists only in the Coulomb field of the nucleus. We have shown that the electromagnetic field can be reduced to a system of independent oscillations (see Chapter Eight), and the energy of an oscillation of frequency v is equal to $hv(n + \frac{1}{2})$. Each unit of n corresponds to a single quantum; but to what does $\frac{1}{2}$ correspond? It is the energy of the zero-point state in which there are no quanta.

If we examine the problem of the oscillations considered in Chapter Three, we see that even in the case of minimum en-

* "Term" is another word for "state."

ergy (in the ground state) the oscillations do not cease; there is no rest. This is a direct consequence of the uncertainty principle. In the same way, the electromagnetic field does not vanish even when there are no quanta. It performs its "zero-point oscillations." In the rigorous theory one cannot say that the field is equal to zero; it is certainly present and acts on every electron. This, however, was not taken into account in the deduction of the energy levels of the hydrogen atom from Dirac's equation.

It is impossible to take this completely into account; but it is possible to find an appropriate formula based on the fact that 1/137 is a small number. The derivation of the formula runs into the following characteristic difficulty. The number of different zero-point oscillations of the field is infinite and each makes its own contribution. Hence the power of the number 1/137, which corresponds to the expected effect in a given approximation, must have an infinite coefficient. Bethe was the first to show how to eliminate this difficulty. If we consider the correction to the energy of a free electron that is not in the field of the nucleus, then for the same reason (the zero-point oscillations of the electromagnetic field) the coefficient of the necessary power of 1/137 will also be infinite. Hence the real correction to the energy in the field of the nucleus will be obtained only if we subtract one infinite result from the other.

The subtraction of one infinite number from another, generally speaking, is not a single-valued operation; but if the requirements of the theory of relativity are carefully observed in the given case we may carry out a completely defined subtraction and, most important, obtain a finite result. This covers the principal part of the effect observed experimentally.

The small residue of about 3 percent is due to the "background" of the electrons with negative energy that surround the given electron. In the field of the nucleus this background is somewhat deformed as if polarized, and the force acting on an electron moving in the field of the nucleus is not strictly a

Coulomb force. The background electrons move away from the nucleus, for they have negative mass. The correction for the "vacuum polarization" exactly covers the 3 percent residue. Experiment confirms the physical reality of the background.

Similarly, we may calculate the correction to the gyromagnetic ratio of the electron and classify all the possible corrections. Thus quantum electrodynamics now has all the main features of a complete physical theory.

Selected readings

Born, M., *Atomic Physics,* Seventh Edition, Hafner, New York, 1962.

Eisberg, R., *Fundamentals of Modern Physics,* Wiley, New York, 1961.

Feynman, R., *Feynman Lectures on Physics,* Vol. III, Addison-Wesley, Reading, Mass., 1964.

Heitler, W., Elementary Wave Mechanics: With Application to Quantum Chemistry, Second Edition, Oxford University Press, New York, 1956.

Park, D., *Introduction to the Quantum Theory,* McGraw-Hill, New York, 1964.

Richtmyer, F. and others, *Introduction to Modern Physics,* Fifth Edition, McGraw-Hill, New York, 1955.

Wehr, M. and J. Richards, Jr., *Physics of the Atom,* Addison-Wesley, Reading, Mass., 1960.

Weidner, R. and R. Sells, *Elementary Modern Physics,* Allyn & Bacon, New York, 1960.

Index